S0-AXS-270

The Roundhouse,
Paradise,
and Mr. Pickering

Books by Dick Perry

RAYMOND AND ME THAT SUMMER
THE ROUNDHOUSE, PARADISE, AND MR. PICKERING

Plays by Dick Perry

GO FROM ME
THE BRIEFCASE BOHEMIAN OF THE 7:54
FOREVER THE WILD SWEET VOICE OF LOVERS

DICK PERRY

The Roundhouse,
Paradise,
and Mr. Pickering

GARDEN CITY, NEW YORK
DOUBLEDAY & COMPANY, INC.
1966

We are grateful to the Louisville & Nashville
Railroad for permission to reprint lines from a
ballad from their film, *The General's Ribbon.*

LIBRARY OF CONGRESS CATALOG CARD NUMBER 66–12235
COPYRIGHT © 1966 BY RICHARD S. PERRY
ALL RIGHTS RESERVED
PRINTED IN THE UNITED STATES OF AMERICA
FIRST EDITION

TO PEGGY

Big steam engine,
Before you go
Let me hear
Your whistle blow . . .

1

It was 2 A.M. and Mr. Pickering was dead, really dead.

An engineer running the Guilford Hill pusher discovered Mr. Pickering's body beside the track. Maybe, when Mr. Pickering was walking to work, the C&O transfer killed him. Maybe the 5301 from the Cincinnati Union Terminal got him.

At first I couldn't believe it. They kid a lot on the third trick and have dumb ideas what is funny. But when the third-trick foreman, Mr. Richter, blew his nose and wiped his eyes, Mr. Pickering's death was a fact.

"The yardmaster is there now," the foreman said. "An ambulance is on the way. But he's dead. He never knew what hit him."

That made sense. Mr. Pickering drank. He lumbered along in a blur. I had never seen him sober and neither had anyone else.

The men took his death hard. One went to the turntable and frowned; another climbed into the cab of a switch engine, sat, and stared in anger; and the Negro from the ashpit kept saying, "Damn . . . damn." Mr. Richter went into his office and shoved papers around his desk. I went to the deadhouse where silence was. Each of us frittered away the night saying good-by to Mr. Pickering as best we could.

Mr. Pickering had been an innocent, filled with shortcomings and booze, who had shuffled unhardened and harmless

1

through life. He was a free spirit who wasn't free. Once he tried to convert a locomotive into a still and make whiskey. "A steam engine is a boiler," he had explained. "I just got to rearrange this bird's plumbing." Once he crashed a locomotive through the roundhouse wall. "I was running the Flyer —and the bird got away from me." Once he ran an electric crane through the street to a church where he tried to get it blessed. "God likes electric cranes. If He hadn't, He would have denounced them."

This was in 1940 and 1941 when the Indiana division of the New York Central System had no diesel locomotives, only steam. The Riverside roundhouse was like any other roundhouse: brick; covered with grime; stalls; and a turntable. The roundhouse was divided into two parts: twenty stalls in the first part, the building ended, there was a gap for the powerhouse spur, and then nine more stalls. These nine stalls were the deadhouse where locomotives were rebuilt.

I sat in the cab of a dismantled Hudson and wondered who would tell Mrs. Bruce and who would empty Mr. Pickering's locker. I wondered what his locker held. A bottle? Mr. Pickering had bottles everywhere. They would be discovering his bottles for years. I watched dawn come through the high windows of the roundhouse and watched the first-trick men assemble: machinists, boilermakers, electricians, pipe fitters, blacksmiths, car knockers, their helpers and apprentices, laborers, and the office men. They stood: talking among themselves. They didn't talk with us because we had nothing in common. They lived in a world where meals were at orderly hours. We could never figure *when* breakfast was.

At seven, the handful of us from the third trick turned in our time cards to the foreman. Mr. Pickering's death had caused work to lag; the first-trick foreman was irritated, but the look in Mr. Richter's eyes said he understood.

Before changing into street clothes I went to the engine dispatcher's office to telephone.

"Kathleen," I said. "It's George."

She was hard to wake up.

2

"What'd you want, George?" she said. "It's seven in the morning and . . ."

"Mr. Pickering is dead."

I heard her gasp.

Then, after a silence, she said in a quiet voice:

"George?"

"Yes?"

"Are you all right?"

"Yeah. But I have to hang up now. I . . ."

"George, are you *sure*? You sound different . . ."

"I *have* to hang up!"

"George . . ."

I hung up.

How could I tell her I was in the dispatcher's office—and crying like a baby?

2

The deadhouse was where I first met Mr. Pickering.

In the deadhouse were locomotives with no rods, no cabs, and no headlights. With fronts open, jackets off, and fire-boxes cold, they were dismembered monsters waiting for men to put them together again.

The Riverside roundhouse worked three shifts. Hundreds of men worked the two tricks from 7 A.M. to 11 P.M. During this period there was no hush, not even in the deadhouse: drills screeched, blacksmiths added to the din, metal clanged against metal, men shouted above the hubbub, and the first two tricks were a Babel. But at eleven, the cater-wauling stopped and we came: a skeleton force who at re-duced speed dawdled away the night. The only noise, at times, was the pant of a locomotive. Sometimes I could walk through the entire roundhouse and not see a soul.

Third-trick men didn't work in the deadhouse. They worked in the twenty-stall part of the roundhouse. There, impatient for the main line, steam riling their iron bellies, locomotives dashed in and out for running repairs. These locomotives endured human tinkering as a man in good health endures an examining physician. They wished only to be serviced quickly and be gone, to feel the pish-pish-pish of the rod-cup gun and the tap-tap-tap of the inspector's hammer—and no nonsense. Yard engines, freight engines, and high-wheeled passenger engines stood side by side,

4

headlights staring in anger, and all sighed terrible sighs, wanting to be free. The engines in the deadhouse, on the other hand, undone and vanquished, had nothing to sigh with.

Well, at 3 A.M., my third day on the third trick and my ninth day as a railroader, I was scrooched down in the fireman's seat of a yard engine in the deadhouse, eating a candy bar, dreaming about Kathleen, and thinking the night would never end. The yard engine had no fire in its firebox, it was not hooked to the direct steam line from the power-house, its main rods were gone, and its tender was some-where else. I wadded up the candy wrapper, tossed it into the firebox, and a voice from *inside* the firebox said:

"Aw. Don't do that."

I think I jumped a mile.

Fireboxes were not meant for people; they were meant for firemen to shovel coal into and make the engine go. The firebox entrance was a round door, a heavy-lidded thing that could shut with a clang. Inside was darkness. But this firebox door was propped open and through it, looking trou-bled, climbed Mr. Pickering.

"You're only a kid," he said.

I was eighteen and said so.

"What kind of bird are you?" he asked. "I don't throw candy wrappers into *your* bedroom, do I?"

"You *sleep* in the firebox?"

"She's cheaper than a boardinghouse."

I gaped with interest. I mean, in the stall next door was an H-10, its feedwater heater missing. Men had been pound-ing on her when I had walked through at ten-thirty that night. On the other side of me was a Mohawk in bad shape: it had no cab. Boilermakers had been shouting at her and cursing. Beyond was a G-46, a switch engine without mean-ing. Pipes dangled from her smokebox like rusted spaghetti. A machinist had been sitting in the open belly of her and hammering. What I'm saying is, the deadhouse, during the

5

other two shifts, wasn't the quietest place. Yet, there was Mr. Pickering, yawning.

He wore dirty overalls and a dirty jumper. They were caked with grease and smelled of sweat. His railroad cap, crusted with engine dirt, was frayed. His face was gray, his eyes were blue, and his breath was Old Grand-Dad. His fingers were stubby, his fingernails were black, and his left thumb was missing. He was short, had a paunch, stood at a tilt; and had he tilted a hair's breadth more, would have toppled.

He wasn't annoyed by my stare. If he angered, he angered out of sight. He had no vanity and made no splash. He was a man born hat in hand. He had quarreled with timidity and lost. He settled into the engineer's seat, looked across at me, yawned some more, and said:

"There's nothing wrong with sleeping there. She has the amenities of a second-rate hotel."

I hadn't thought of it that way.

"Birds at railroad boardinghouses don't have her half so good," he mumbled.

My father had told me about railroading boardinghouses: some were nice, some were not, and none was the Ritz.

"Don't you ever go home?" I said. "What about your wife?"

"Got no wife."

"Your mother?"

"Got no mother."

"You're *alone* in the world?"

"There's always Rosalind," he said.

After he said *Rosalind* he closed his eyes. With his eyes closed, he said:

"How do you feel about fat women?"

"I don't know," I said.

"Think about fat women a minute," he said. "*Then* tell me how you feel."

I had not known many. Besides it was 3 A.M. But my silence didn't bother him.

6

"Rosalind is the fattest woman there is," he said. "She's a bird."

"Swell," I said.

He opened his eyes and looked at me.

"You got a woman?"

"I *go* with a girl," I said.

"How fat?"

"She *isn't* fat."

"Skin and bones?"

I changed the subject.

"Do you always sleep in fireboxes?"

He thought about this.

"Well, yeah. You might say," he said, and pointed to the engine on the next track. "Yesterday I slept in her. Last week I had a switch engine they wasn't supposed to work on. Only some second-trick machinist woke me up, pounding inches from my head." Mr. Pickering looked exhausted. "That's no way to run a railroad," he said. His voice was filled with melancholy.

But it held no anger. Night made third-trick men placid creatures. The silence lulled them. Compared to the hurry of the other shifts, third-trick men were tortoises in a world of rabbits. They didn't march through the night; they straggled, hibernated on their feet, took their time, napped, loitered, and nodded among themselves. They came to work tired and went home tired.

Mr. Pickering was no exception. He lapsed into silence. That didn't bother me. Third-trick conversations were slow-motion dialogues filled with silences. Why hurry a sleepy conversation? Talk killed time and time needed killing. I thought for a minute that Mr. Pickering had gone to sleep, but I was wrong. After two minutes, without opening his eyes, he said:

"I'm Beershot."

"Mr. *Beershot?*"

"Don't be a bird," he said. "My name is Pickering. They just *call* me Beershot."

7

"Mr. Pickering?"

He thought about getting irritated but thought better of it.

"You *are* a bird," he said. "What happens is, I go into bars and say 'Gimme-a-shot-and-a-beer,' and the guys here know that. So they call me Beershot. Nobody calls me *Mr.* Pickering."

That seemed sad. I was about to comment, but didn't. Mr. Pickering wouldn't have heard.

He was asleep—for real.

⋯⋯◦❦◦ 3 ◦❦◦⋯⋯

Mr. Pickering, railroad machinist, was forty-seven years old when he died. He was born August 1, 1894, the day the war started between China and Japan. His father was born the day street cleaners demolished the merchants' stalls on Fifth Street. That date: February 24, 1870. Mr. Pickering, every chance he could, associated his life to history. "When I was three," he told me, "I got a red wagon and Spain declared war on the United States." So to keep the record intact, Mr. Pickering died August 18, 1941, and Congress extended the draft to eighteen months.

On February 24, 1912, the same day Teddy Roosevelt said he would accept the Republican nomination for president, Mr. Pickering hired out on the New York Central. "I did better than him," Mr. Pickering said. "Taft got the nomination."

When Mr. Pickering died he had been with the railroad twenty-nine years. This allowed him the seniority to work at least the 3 P.M. to 11 P.M. shift, but he said, "What's the use of them hours? I got no home to go to."

Besides, he liked to drink.

"Birds who work the first trick can't go into bars in the morning," he said. "*I* can. Show me another guy that can wet his whistle at 8 A.M. and get away with it."

I didn't argue. I liked him and, anyway, I was a Lit. Major. I was the only Lit. Major in the roundhouse and since Lit.

9

Majors are supposed to be in college, majoring in literature, I should explain why I wasn't.

Well, the roundhouse was in Sedamsville, a railroad community in the Ohio Valley. Because my father had been a fireman on the New York Central, I had been raised in the shadow of the roundhouse smokestack. Sedamsville wasn't a proud community. It was a sad little street lined with sad little shops. People who lived in Sedamsville said they didn't. Every other business was a saloon. Added to the noise of the railroad was the noise of the streetcars and the trucks. Noise was Sedamsville's chief product. When the banging of boxcars didn't deafen us, the din of passing freight trains did. Silences used to make my father sit up in bed and shout:

"What happened?"

Then one boxcar would slam into another—and my father would go back to sleep again.

It wasn't Sedamsville's fault that it was grimy; railroad communities always were. My father said railroading was in his blood; my mother said it was in every wash she hung out. Cinders and soot settled everywhere, and when my mother grew flowers, they blossomed gray. So much for Sedamsville. But let me explain about railroading.

I didn't hate it; I simply didn't understand it. Oh, I used to get excited when the New York Central calendars came, but they stopped coming in 1931. They were beautiful. The 1924 calendar called "Where the Centuries Pass in the Night" showed the eastbound and westbound Twentieth Century Limiteds passing each other somewhere. I was only two in 1924 but my father saved it for me. He saved them all: the 1925 calendar that showed the Twentieth Century Limited in a snowstorm, the 1928 calendar that showed three locomotives side by side because the Twentieth Century Limited that day was running extra sections, and the last calendar in 1931, which also showed the Twentieth Century Limited and was called "Morning on the Mohawk."

10

Railroad men called the Twentieth Century Limited the Flyer. When I asked my father why, he gave me a look.

No matter how much I knew about railroading, somebody knew more. For instance, in the seventh grade when I tried to impress the science class, I said that a steam locomotive was a boiler and that somehow the steam made the wheels turn and the whistle blow. After I said this, which was all I knew about railroading then, a girl said that the New York Central's first 4-8-4 wheel arrangement was the locomotive called the Niagra. She said that the Niagra had seventy-five inch driver wheels and was equipped with specially designed side rods.

None of this explains what a Lit. Major was doing in a roundhouse. Well, in high school I got the writing bug, but they wouldn't let me on the school newspaper because I had written a letter to the editor which said the school newspaper should be abolished. But in high school I did meet Kathleen—she was a junior when I was a senior—and told her I was going to write the Great American Novel, which I must get around to someday. This impressed her. Her father worked for the New York Central, too, but in an office, and had something to do with lost freight cars. She lived in Sayler Park in a clean house on a clean street; didn't know the grim of railroading, its roar didn't touch her; and *Finlandia* had more meaning to her than a hotbox. Seeing her walking along and kicking leaves—well, you have your idea of beauty and I won't disturb it, but *she* was mine. Kathleen was a slim, good-natured girl, had brown eyes, drank orange juice for breakfast, was good in school, played the organ in church, and smelled like soap.

Kathleen and I made satisfying plans: I was going to the University of Cincinnati, study writing, grow a beard, and be a bohemian. She was going to the College of Music, study music, and be a concert pianist. We would get married, live in a garret, and eat cheese; only two days after I graduated from high school, my father died, which pulled the plug out of everything.

11

My father's death left me and my mother with a bunch of calendars that showed the Twentieth Century Limited— and that was all. The depression had exhausted most of our money, ended my father's insurance program; what money was left the funeral took, and there you are.

A man who had been my father's friend said:

"They're hiring at the roundhouse. You could get on as a laborer."

Kathleen and I took a long walk and talked about it. She could sense my mood was glum.

"Are you afraid?" she said.

"Yes," I said.

"I wish I could change the world," she said and squeezed my hand. "Take a year off. Things will work out, George. I know they will."

Three days later I was in the roundhouse.

That's how a Lit. Major became a railroad man, but don't feel gloomy. Sherwood Anderson used to write advertising copy in Chicago.

"I remember when you came on the third trick," Mr. Pickering said. "We talked about fat women—and the Germans occupied Paris."

＊＊＊＊＊ ❧❦ **4** ❧❦ ＊＊＊＊＊

I didn't know a Mogul from a Mallet (they're *kinds* of locomotives, I know now) but I did know not to step in front
of trains, to say "sir" to my elders, and that when the roundhouse whistle tooted, it tooted for me.

The whistle was always tooting. It tooted for the first trick
to start so loud its toot echoed from the Kentucky hills across
the river. Sedamsville used its toots for an alarm clock.

It tooted at 11 A.M. for first-trick lunch to begin; twenty
minutes later to end the lunch; at two fifty-five—two short
toots—to end the first trick's day; at three to start the second
trick; at seven for the second-trick lunch; at seven-twenty
to end the lunch; at ten fifty-five to end the second trick itself; and at eleven to start the third trick. Then it didn't
toot again until six fifty-five to finish the third trick and at
seven to start the cycle over again, seven days a week.

And sometimes it tooted *unexpectedly* to bewilder Sedamsville because Sedamsville, which needed something to
believe in, believed in roundhouse toots.

Mr. Burkholder, the general foreman of the Riverside
roundhouse, wasn't impressed that I intended to be a Lit.
Major. Something awful had happened to him: he had been
promoted from the ranks of men to the ranks of management and left ill at ease. He wore a brown suit. He wore a
cloth cap. His face was long and he tried to hide his melancholy with a scowl.

13

He helped me complete the employment forms; became withdrawn as our interview progressed; and by the time I told him I wanted to write the Great American Novel, he stopped talking and looked pained.

Finally, he said:

"We'll start you as a laborer on the third trick. You'll run the turntable."

"Running the turntable sounds like fun," I said.

He looked sadder than ever.

He waggled a finger, which meant I was to follow him, and I did. We walked through the roundhouse to the foreman of the first trick. He was a younger replica of Mr. Burkholder, but he was not as disenchanted. He still had visions of rising through the ranks to presidency of the railroad. He didn't know what Mr. Burkholder knew: that as he bubbled to the top he would meet, head on, others bubbling to the bottom, all the bubbles would break, and that's the trouble with corporate life.

The plan called for me to work the day shift for a week, master the turntable, then go to the third trick, where new laborers began.

"Running the turntable sounds like fun," I told the first-trick foreman.

He, too, looked pained.

We went to the turntable. The plaque said it was a "Bethlehem Twin Span," was 110 feet long, had a 108-foot wheel base, a capacity of 432 tons, and had been built in 1926. I'll bet that girl in my seventh-grade science class didn't know *that*.

Sitting in the turntable's control shack and eating an apple was Mr. Martin. He was an old man who had the eyes of an angry goldfish.

"Work with this kid a week," the first-trick foreman said. "Teach him everything about the turntable. He'll run it on the third trick next week."

Mr. Martin's eyes became angrier.

"Hah!" he snorted.

14

Mr. Martin's problem was he had worked at the Riverside roundhouse longer than any other laborer. He was a wrinkled cherub who didn't care that younger laborers had been promoted over him and earned more money. He liked being the oldest laborer. Had he not been the oldest laborer at the roundhouse, he would have been the oldest messenger Postal Telegraph had. Other than having pride in being the oldest, he bickered, demanded rights others had forgotten, and on his day off sat in the park and glared at women.

He was sixty-three years old, he liked apples, he still had some of his teeth; and those he lacked he had acquired from a friend who died but they fit. Mr. Pickering said that when Mr. Martin was sixteen he had married a redhead named Dorothy, who died giving birth to their child. In 1907 the child—a redheaded boy—died, too; and Mr. Martin vowed never to marry again. He married again in 1909 and his second wife ran off with a brakeman. He married again in 1911 and his third wife got run over by a Model T Ford. He married again in 1912 and that marriage lasted three years. He refused to say how it ended or why. After that, he concentrated on railroading.

"Running the turntable is an art," he complained to the foreman. "It'll take more than a week for the kid to learn it."

"I can teach him in ten minutes," said the foreman.

"Not to run the turntable *right*," Mr. Martin said.

"Do the best you can," said the foreman.

"I'll need four years."

"In four years we can make him a machinist!"

"Machinists are slobs!" Mr. Martin shouted.

But the foreman was halfway back to the roundhouse.

"And so are boilermakers," Mr. Martin screamed after him. "And pipe fitters and car knockers and electricians. They're all slobs!"

Disgusted, Mr. Martin turned to me.

"Well," he said. "What have *you* got to say?"

I wanted to start on the right foot.

"Running the turntable," I said, "sounds like fun."

15

He looked pained, too.

We went inside the turntable shanty, where the main control was: a control knob the same as streetcar motormen twirl. Push it to the right, the table revolves one way; push it to the left, the table revolves the other; return it to center and the turntable stops. The only other control was a hand brake. When the turntable tracks are lined up with the correct track, pull the hand brake and there you are. Well, there was one *other* control: the light switch. Push it up and the shanty light goes on. Put it down, the light goes off.

"The thing to remember," Mr. Martin said, "is not to signal an engine on to the table if the table ain't ready. That's important."

"Yes, sir."

"And never throw apple cores in the turntable pit."

"Yes, sir."

"Now, here's how she works."

He released the hand brake, moved the control knob, and the table turned. Its electric motor—geared to move a 176-ton passenger locomotive or an 84-ton yard engine with equal ease—groaned a powerful groan. As the table turned, Mr. Martin pulled out a red railroad handkerchief, wiped his forehead, and said:

"Railroading takes a lot out of a man."

"Yes, sir."

"Are you making fun of me?" he demanded.

"No, sir."

He chewed this thought a moment.

"Kid, I'll tell you something you must never repeat." He looked out the window as the table moved. He made sure no one was near. "There's nothing to it. But never let on, or they'll abolish the job."

"I'll never tell."

"And," he added, "you're right. Running the turntable *is* fun. It . . ."

He would have said more but the roundhouse whistle tooted.

16

"*Lunch!*" he shouted and stopped the table. "Come on, kid, *hurry!*"

He leaped off the turntable and scampered stiff-legged to the roundhouse. He was an unarticulated Mercury and his target was food.

"Come on, kid, *faster!*"

It was pleasant inside the roundhouse during lunch. A quiet filled the place. The hammering, screeching, and shouting dwindled into silence. Lunchtime gentled the locomotives, too. They were at peace. Somewhere down the line the forward pump on one throbbed—like a heart beating.

Mr. Martin said:

"Turntables *are* important. Without turntables, there'd be no engines in the roundhouse. The slobs never consider that."

He frowned at his apple.

"Running the turntable *is* an art, kid. If it wasn't, why would I devote a lifetime to it?"

I spent the week learning his art. The turntable had only three controls: a control knob, a hand brake, and a light switch. Mr. Martin, who had mastered them, passed his knowledge to me.

Then I went to the third trick and met Mr. Pickering.

5

I met Mr. Pickering the first night when he had been sleeping in the firebox. But it wasn't until the second night that I realized what kind of person he was.

The second night was hot and stuffy. No air circulated. Even the stars twinkled hot. I sat on the turntable, sweating, and I wished it would rain. But there were no clouds.

I saw Mr. Pickering approach from the deadhouse. He lugged a canvas deck chair, folded; he stumbled vaguely over a rail, looked back at it with surprise, and in a minute, he stood before me, hesitated, and said:

"Where's Duveneck?"

"Up at the coal dock," I said. "You know: shadowboxing."

"To each his own," Mr. Pickering said.

I wondered if he liked Mr. Duveneck. Not many men could. Mr. Duveneck was the third-trick hostler and hostlers led lives of frustration. They were thwarted dreamers who dreamed a losing game. They ran locomotives only between the roundhouse and the coal dock, a half mile away. They never whistled at a country crossing; they never waved at pretty girls; they never got to yank back the throttle and make the locomotive go fast. Mr. Duveneck, the third-trick hostler, relieved his frustrations by shadowboxing. I don't know what the other hostlers did.

Mr. Duveneck also played football every evening, ate raw hamburger, wrote fan letters to Charles Atlas, and did head-

18

stands. He was thirty-five years old. He was single. He was a peacock of a man. He had so much self-confidence he made me sick.

The first time I had met Mr. Duveneck, I had gone out to the turntable shanty and there he was, shadowboxing the moon.

He struck a pose, protected himself at all times from the planets, and said:

"Relax, kid. I'm Duveneck, the hostler."

"Oh," I said.

"How many push-ups can you do?" he said.

"I don't know," I said.

Well, we stood around and talked some more. He did most of the talking. He explained about muscle tone and how good he was at everything. He said that if he had boxed in the Golden Glove matches he would have won the championship hands down. He said he knew more about baseball than the New York Yankees and Cincinnati Reds combined.

"I really should be in the majors," he said. And he said, "I would have made a great Olympic swimmer, but water gets in my nose." He was a broad-shouldered Adonis and admitted it. His teeth were so white he smiled all the time. "And," he said, "I got muscles some guys never thought of." I got a kick out of him, but I didn't let on. He was a blowhard whose feelings could be crushed with a look.

That was the way Mr. Duveneck was. And, after Mr. Pickering arrived with the folded deck chair, Mr. Duveneck walked on to the turntable platform, too.

"Aw, Beershot," he said. "Not again."

Mr. Pickering cleared his throat. He was nervous.

"It's one-thirty, Duveneck," he said. "Most of the engines are in that's going in. You only got that yard engine waiting at the ashpit. And if we get the three out that has to be out, that leaves nearly three hours. I'll help," he added hopefully.

"Why don't Rosalind buy an electric fan?" Mr. Duveneck protested.

"You know how she is," said Mr. Pickering. "How about it?"

"Well," said Mr. Duveneck, "Okay. But not *every* night."

"Sure," said Mr. Pickering.

Mr. Duveneck glared up the track at the Mogul by the ashpit. "Let's shake a leg, kid," he said. "We'll run her in stall sixteen." He glared at me. "Then line up for stall three to get that H-7 out of there. We got work to do."

He hurried up the track to the switch engine.

Mr. Pickering, on the turntable walkway, tried to unfold the deck chair.

As the table revolved to line up with the ashpit track, I leaned out of the shanty window and said:

"Mr. Pickering, what has that deck chair to do with moving these engines around? And what did Mr. Duveneck mean when he said why doesn't she buy an electric fan? And what . . ."

"You'll see," he said, struggling with the deck chair. It wouldn't unfold right.

I pulled the hand brake and signaled Mr. Duveneck; while he backed the switch engine on to the turntable, I tried to help Mr. Pickering with the deck chair. I wasn't much help. The engine rumbled on to the turntable and Mr. Duveneck glared at me from its cab. He glared *smiling*. His teeth, you know.

"Never mind that chair," he shouted. "Stall sixteen!"

He wanted to run the locomotive into the roundhouse while it still had steam to make it go. The engine had no way of making more steam: its fire had been dumped at the ashpit. When it used what steam was in its boiler, it was through. Hostlers hate locomotives that are low on steam. When that happens, the locomotive headlight burns a dim yellow because there isn't enough steam to turn the generator fast enough. And if the engine can move at all, it creeps as if each turn of its drivers is the last. And when it stops, it stops for good.

Engineers didn't face this problem. An engineer could

20

shout across the engine cab at his fireman to shovel more coal, add more water, and make more steam. Hostlers, alone in the cab, had no firemen to shout at. Worse, the engines hostlers ran seldom had fires. There was only enough steam in the engine to run into the house or back to the ashpit. "Show me an engineer who could run one of these babies when there ain't no pressure," Mr. Duveneck liked to brag. "I know tricks they never thought of. I can run 'em when they ain't got steam enough to steam open a letter. I can run 'em when their boilers is ice cold." He bragged a lot; some of the things he bragged were impossible, but a fact is a fact: hostlers *were* magicians. They ran engines when regular engineers wouldn't even try. I was proud of hostlers.

I turned the turntable to stall sixteen; the Mogul limped into the roundhouse; and I trailed after it. I carried a great Stillson wrench. Once the engine stopped inside the round-house, I manhandled an adjustable pipe to connect it to the blowoff cock of the locomotive. This pipe—the direct-steam line—came from the ceiling. There it connected with an even bigger pipe that came from the powerhouse, where there was always steam. I tightened the pipe connections, linking the powerhouse and the engine, and opened a high-hanging valve on the steam line. "Direct steaming" they called it—and only a few roundhouses had it. With no fire in its firebox to make its own steam, the locomotive, via the powerhouse steam source, needed an intravenous feeding.

By the time the roundhouse crew had serviced the Mogul —washed its boilers, wiped its headlight, and greased its rods—the Mogul would have, by these feedings, sufficient steam in its belly; the pipe would be disconnected, and the engine would chug, with just enough steam to reach to the ashpit, out of the roundhouse again. There a new fire would be kindled in its innards; it would again be a self-contained power plant with a red-hot gut and no further need of men.

Well, after hooking up the pipe to the locomotive in stall sixteen, I lodged a length of chain in front and back of one of its driver wheels. That way the unattended engine

21

wouldn't creep out of the roundhouse and run away. I went to stall three, undid that engine's pipe, went to the turntable, lined up the tracks, and Mr. Duveneck backed that engine out. I turned the table so the engine pointed to the ashpit track and, as Mr. Duveneck hurried the engine off the table, he bellowed:

"Unhook the one in seven. We got to get her out, too."

"Not for three hours," I bellowed back.

"Unhook her!" he bellowed—and the H-7 chugged off the turntable.

For the next hour we worked like demons. We pulled out every engine that had to be out by 7 A.M. and they began to stack up at the ashpit. The Negro who started fires in them complained he could start only so many fires at a time, but Mr. Duveneck ignored him and kept bringing engines out. Finally, all finished, Mr. Duveneck glared at Mr. Pickering, who, in that hour, had solved the mystery of the deck chair: he had unfolded it.

"Next time," Mr. Duveneck said, "tell Rosalind to buy an electric fan."

Then he shadowboxed up to the coal docks and, because all his work was done, I didn't see him again until dawn.

I didn't have time to miss him.

"Uh . . . uh . . ." said Mr. Pickering. He stared off in the opposite direction.

"Yes?" I said.

"Here comes Rosalind," he said.

She walked out of the darkness into the turntable's light, looked at Mr. Pickering with hate, and snapped:

"Are you getting any?"

I recognized her right away. Rosalind was Mrs. Bruce.

Mrs. Bruce lived at the other end of Sedamsville. She lived in a frame cottage that had four rooms and a front porch that sagged. The house was gray with railroad grime. It hadn't been painted in twenty years. She had a husband somewhere, no one had seen him lately, and Mrs. Bruce was too busy with gentlemen callers to miss him. She was, ac-

22

cording to my mother, a fallen woman. She sat on her front porch and waved at streetcar motormen. When streetcars weren't going by, she leaned out her back window and waved at brakemen. Sometimes these men visited her. They went inside her house, stayed fifteen minutes, and came out looking drained.

She was what Mr. Pickering said: fat beyond all expectations. She flourished in fat; she was enormous; her size overwhelmed me. She made a lie of fat people: she wasn't jolly, couldn't stomach kindness, was irritating, spiteful, and went out of her way to badger mailmen. A big woman, she operated as a small child: loathing everything and everybody every minute of every day. Mr. Pickering said once, "There is not a kind bone in her body, but there's a lot of woman somewhere in that fat." She reminded me of grease, tallow, and blubber—but it wasn't my place to criticize. She was old enough to be my mother.

Now that Mrs. Bruce has entered, we must get one thing straight. There will be no cursing in this book, and Mrs. Bruce cursed all the time. Her conversations were larded with curse words. She seemed preoccupied with sexual intercourse and bowel movements. I tried using blanks for these words but that didn't help much. Once she said:

"That —— —— of a —— —— —— waiter —— —— mother's —— —— and —— with his —— —— old —— and his —— —— rusty —— —— and his —— —— father's —— —— ——'s —— the —— nerve —— and —— warmer than —— —— —— on a —— —— in —— winter —— —— beer!"

What she meant was:

"Please tell the waiter he brought me a warm beer."

So I will eliminate her speech characteristics because they add little to the book, slow the action, and besides, embarrass me.

Anyway, Mrs. Bruce was not all bad. In fact, on the subject of Mrs. Bruce the mothers in Sedamsville had, among themselves, reached an understanding. It was an understanding without malice. A cruel thing had happened to

23

Mrs. Bruce. Long ago, about the time I was born, Mrs. Bruce had gone to the hospital to have a baby. That was when there had been a Mr. Bruce on the scene. Her baby died in childbirth. Mrs. Bruce went to pieces. She thought God took her baby away and had only hidden it. She thought God did this to get even with her because she waved at streetcar motormen. "It was like she stopped caring," my mother said. That was when Mrs. Bruce began to get fat. Unable to wipe away her tears or stop her from waving at streetcar motormen, Mr. Bruce left and never returned.

One time when I was a child, my father and I were sitting in a Sedamsville bar. He was drinking beer and I was drinking a Coke. Mrs. Bruce—sloppy, fat, and disheveled—came in and looked around. She wasn't looking for a man. There was despair in her eyes. She was looking for her baby. She looked for her baby a lot and that was pretty sad.

Some nights, drunk and lonesome, she used to walk up and down the streets and whisper:

"Baby . . . baby . . . baby . . ."

I guess labor pains make lodge members of all mothers, and it was as I said: Sedamsville mothers forgave her, made allowances for her, and granted her one reprieve after another. But their forgiveness was not enough. She could not forgive herself. So she drank, got fatter, and tried to blot out each transgression with another. She waddled stony-hearted into middle age and was the loneliest person I had ever known.

And there she was on the turntable, glaring at Mr. Pickering and me.

After her greeting, she plopped down into the deck chair, hiked her dress up over her fat knees, and sprawled out, gasping in the heat.

"I'll start her," Mr. Pickering said to Mrs. Bruce. "You'll be cool in a minute, Rosalind."

All she did was curse.

"You can ride her a couple of hours," Mr. Pickering said. "All the engines is out."

24

She cursed some more.

He turned the control knob; the turntable began to move, and he motioned for me to step off with him and let it go around by itself. The table didn't turn fast; stepping off was easy.

"Can't you make this thing twirl faster," Mrs. Bruce complained. "It don't stir up no air at all. Seems to me you could goose this thing and make it go . . ."

Her voice faded as the table rotated her away from us.

Mr. Pickering motioned me to follow him to the dead-house.

"She likes to be alone on hot nights," he explained.

We sat in the deadhouse darkness and watched the turntable go around and around. We could hardly distinguish Mrs. Bruce in the moonlight. But I suppose riding the turntable *was* cooler than sitting in one spot. Breeze had to be somewhere.

"Maybe," said Mr. Pickering, "now she can get some sleep, the poor little thing . . ."

6

"There is fifty birds for each man, woman, and child on earth," said Mr. Pickering. "Somewhere is forty-nine others that belong to me."

"Huh," I said.

I had discovered him at 4 A.M. in the locker room. He was mixing a concoction in a coffee cup: the yolk of a hard-boiled egg, bread crumbs, and milk. I had asked him what he was making. That had been his answer.

Lunch was over, he and I were alone, no engines waited at the ashpit, the men on running repair dozed in locomotive cabs, and the third-trick foreman, Mr. Richter, was in his office, door closed, resting his eyes.

"I'll show you what I mean," Mr. Pickering said.

I followed him to the deadhouse. We stopped at a yard engine that had new main rods.

"Hold this," Mr. Pickering said. He handed me the cup of glop. He climbed up into the cab of the engine, reached down, and said, "Hand her up." I handed him the cup and climbed up to see what he was doing. He walked back into the empty tender, the thing that trails the engine and holds its coal and water. This one had no coal.

He got out his flashlight and said:

"Don't scare her."

I saw nothing.

"Scare who?" I said.

"Look," he said.

He shined the light on a shoe box. Inside the box, looking irritated, was a baby sparrow. It twittered a baby twitter, opened its mouth, and gasped for food.

"The poor little thing fell out of her nest," Mr. Pickering said. "I found her this morning. She's got to be fed every half hour she's awake."

Mr. Pickering dabbed gobs of glop on to the end of a toothpick, the sparrow opened wider, and *plop!* in went the food. Mr. Pickering, as every railroad machinist could, could swing a sledgehammer with the precision of an angry artist. But when he fed the sparrow, his hand trembled.

"I don't know much about birds," he said. "This morning I mixed Old Grand-Dad in her food. It was the first time I heard a sparrow cough."

He wasn't supposed to know much about birds. The roundhouse was not meant to be a bird sanctuary. But birds were there. When you build a room to hold dozens of locomotives, you build a room that's big. The roundhouse ceiling was thirty feet high. Each of the twenty-nine tracks into the roundhouse had its own set of double doors: fourteen feet wide and nearly twenty-six feet high. In summer when these great doors were propped open, birds swooped in and out. They sang mating calls to the bells that dinged. They flew through clouds of steam. They had themselves a ball. But in winter, when the great doors were closed to keep out the wind and snow, the sparrows stayed inside. They refused to go out. The world was their dinner plate. When the world was hot they searched weeds for seeds and insects. When the world was cold they lived off the crumbs from ham sandwiches.

The roundhouse wasn't the brightest and cleanest birdhouse built. During the day, dim light filtered through unwashed windows. There was never enough light to work by. Electric bulbs burned twenty-four hours a day. The bulbs dotted the faraway ceiling—and above them, unseen in the gloom, was a tangle of rafters and pipes. In this dirty never-

27

never land high above the world, sparrows nested. They warmed themselves in patches of sunlight on the round-house floor. They drank the water that dribbled from the locomotives. They were unmoved by the noises that locomotives made. They never wondered where summer went or why the great doors were closed. Generations of sparrows had lived in the roundhouse. It was all they knew. They thought the rest of the world was steamy and noisy, too.

"Last Christmas," said Mr. Pickering, "I scattered sunflower seeds around for them. She was the best Christmas the poor little things ever had."

He kept feeding the baby sparrow.

"They don't have her easy," he said. "Birds have got to watch their step every minute of their lives. It's a wonder they ain't nervous wrecks."

When the bird was fed, Mr. Pickering straightened up, looked melancholy, and said:

"Now I got to do something that goes against my grain."

He climbed down from the engine, walked around to the front of it, and flipped open the tin cover of the work report hanging there. The work report was a printed form. Machinists initialed it when they had completed a specific job. When all the repairs listed on the work report were done and initialed, the locomotive was returned to service.

Mr. Pickering—deliberately—erased a machinist's initials. The machinist had signed to say the main rods had been replaced.

"No," I protested.

"Yes," he said.

"But *why?*"

"I'd rather not talk about her," he said.

"But that means another machinist will do the job over again!"

"The important thing, kid, is they don't move the engine till that poor little thing can fly."

Well, this went on for four days. Each night Mr. Pickering

28

fed the sparrow and erased the machinist's initials. Each morning the foreman who wanted to be president of the railroad walked along the line, read the work sheets on each locomotive, and assigned tasks to the first-trick machinists. Each day a new crew put new main rods on Mr. Pickering's switch engine, initialed the job as completed, and each night Mr. Pickering erased the initials to start the round again.

I asked him why nobody caught on. He explained that locomotives came in and out around the clock and that the men were moved from job to job each day. Engines *did* look alike: that is, one H-10 looked the same as any other H-10; and that held for the other kinds, too. The machinists who pulled the main rods on Mr. Pickering's birdhouse were surprised each time to discover the old rods as good as new —in fact, they looked *brand new,* which they were—but the machinists didn't question their assignment. They weren't company men. They had come to put in eight hours. It was the foreman's job to run the roundhouse. Anything they could do to humor him was all right with them.

If Mr. Duveneck, the hostler, hadn't been nosing around, Mr. Pickering could have gone on until the sparrow retired on a pension. But, during the lunch hour on the fourth night, Mr. Duveneck's nosiness got triggered.

Third-trick lunch hours were ceremonial things. Nobody ate lunch then. Sometimes we napped right through the lunch hour. There was no loud roundhouse whistle to wake us at 3 A.M.; it would have awakened all of Sedamsville, too. At 3 A.M., Mr. Richter, the third-trick foreman, stepped outside his office and pulled on a rope that was suspended from the ceiling. This rope was attached to a whistle *inside* the roundhouse. It tooted no haunting toot. It bleated only an anemic bleat. Men standing ten feet away couldn't hear it. That's why, rather than miss lunch, third-trick men put down their tools and began to assemble by the foreman's door at one-thirty. They'd linger, pretend to be busy, and while waiting, eat their lunches. Then the foreman would come out at three, pull the rope, the whistle would bleat,

29

and the twenty-minute lunch hour would start. Having eaten their lunches by this time, the men crawled into locomotive cabs and took naps.

Mr. Richter stayed in his office, his door shut tight, between one-thirty and three because he didn't want to come out and embarrass the men who were standing around, eating ham sandwiches, and waiting for lunch. Sometimes, though, Mr. Richter forgot to come out at three and this irritated the men. They would begin to talk loud and bang things, which did the trick. The office door would open, Mr. Richter would stagger out, yawn, pull the whistle rope, stagger back into his office, and close the door again. On these nights the men talked about reporting him to the union but they never did.

What I'm saying is, when lunch hour came at 3 A.M., the locker room where we ate was empty. There were no lunches left to be eaten.

Well, on the fourth night, just Mr. Pickering and I were there. I was wishing for a Pepsi-Cola and thinking about Kathleen; and Mr. Pickering was stirring another cup of glop. The roundhouse was quiet. The only sounds were a shower faucet dripping, the click of Mr. Pickering's spoon against the cup, and the distant banging of boxcars in the yards.

But the locker-room door opened and Mr. Duveneck came in. He stared in wonder at what Mr. Pickering was mixing.

"Gruel!" he said. There was distaste in his voice. "Beershot, if you had teeth like mine, you wouldn't need that pap. You could chew raw steaks."

He showed us his teeth to prove it.

"That's not for Mr. Pickering," I started to say. "It's for . . ."

But Mr. Pickering shot me a worried look.

Please, his look said, *no.*

Mr. Duveneck was perplexed. He hated to be perplexed. "What's going on?" he complained.

30

"Nothing," said Mr. Pickering.

"If it ain't for you, who's it for?"

"Forget it," said Mr. Pickering.

"Hmmmmmmmmm," said Mr. Duveneck. To relieve his tensions, he began to shadowbox a locker door.

Pretty soon he left, but his nosiness was a cloud over our heads.

The glop was ready, but we waited.

"Until the coast is clear," Mr. Pickering sighed.

When it was, we went to feed the bird. As I watched Mr. Pickering shovel glop at the sparrow, I said:

"I was sure peeved with Mr. Duveneck back there. He makes me mad. Why don't you get mad at him?"

Mr. Pickering, concentrating on the bird, said absently:

"Aw, Mr. Duveneck is an angel."

"Mr. Duveneck—the hostler?" I cried. "The guy who shadowboxes? The guy who shows his teeth? The guy who . . ."

"Never mind," said Mr. Pickering.

Embarrassed he climbed out of the engine, walked to the work sheet, and erased the machinist's initials. That meant, once again, the main rods would be changed. Avoiding my eyes, Mr. Pickering sat on the engine's bumper step. He didn't want to talk about it, but he felt he had to explain.

"It's a game I play," he said. He sounded distressed. "I pretend everybody is angels."

He fingered the empty cup. He was nervous. A grown man hates to bare his soul to a kid.

"I mean, take a street full of people," he said. "*They're* angels. You know, only they got their wings tucked in." He looked to see if I was going to laugh. I wasn't. "It makes the world nicer," he concluded, sorry he had mentioned the matter.

"If Mr. Duveneck ever heard you," I said, "he would tease you from here to . . ."

"I know, I *know*," Mr. Pickering said. "I didn't even want to tell you. But she slipped out. And I had to explain."

31

Mr. Pickering was defenseless. But how could I poke fun at a man who considered Mr. Duveneck and everybody else as angels? The thought of it made the world cleaner somehow, and sweeter. I pictured Vine Street in Cincinnati crowded with Mr. Pickering's angels: shoving, pushing, waiting for green lights, window-shopping, hurrying for a late appointment, and panhandling. They were bums, housewives, newsboys, school girls, junior clerks, streetcar conductors, and bank presidents . . . and each one an angel! It made pleasant pretending, turned soreheads into reasonable creatures, and justified each child there was.

I was about to tell Mr. Pickering this. And I was going to tell him his secret was safe with me. But, before I could say a word, he had shuffled away. Make fun of him? Never. He had populated Cincinnati with angels, turned the roundhouse into paradise, and to make fun would have undone these things: turning them back into the ordinary—and would have caused the death of angels.

"Angels!"

I turned. I was surprised and afraid. Mr. Duveneck, shadowboxing and showing his teeth, hustled around from behind the engine and looked with scorn at the departing Mr. Pickering.

"Angels!" he sneered again—and spit.

Mr. Pickering, lost in his private world, hadn't seen or heard Mr. Duveneck. Mr. Pickering was gone.

I looked at Mr. Duveneck. I didn't know how much he had heard. All I knew was, it was hard to consider him an angel.

"Quit picking on him," I said.

Mr. Duveneck jabbed left hooks at a passenger engine.

"Someday," he said, "Beershot is going to get himself into *real* trouble. Walking around and talking about *angels!* Kid, you got to stay clear of that freak."

Mr. Duveneck was delivering imaginary body blows to the locomotive.

"What's Beershot up to this time?" he said. He was burning with nosiness.

"Nothing," I said.

"Yeah? He's up to *something*," Mr. Duveneck said. He shadowboxed away from me and out of the deadhouse.

Well, it would have been nice if I could write here that Mr. Pickering kept the engine tied up until the sparrow flew away. But I can't. The roundhouse wasn't that simple. The next night I walked through the deadhouse; Mr. Pickering's engine was gone.

I ran outside. There it sat: on the coal dock lead. It was snorting, puffing, dripping, throbbing, pumping—it was alive. And its tender was heaped with coal.

I saw it at one-forty. I felt sick. I hurried, looking for Mr. Pickering. How do you tell a guy like that his plan wasn't good enough? What do you say to a guy when they've buried his sparrow alive? I looked for him, but I didn't want to find him. Does that make sense?

Men were gathering outside the foreman's office for their lunch hour. They ate ham sandwiches and stared at the whistle rope. But Mr. Pickering was not among them. Neither was Mr. Duveneck. I passed by the men; they didn't say hello; neither did I; that was standard, though. It was silly to say hello each time men passed one another in the roundhouse. At first *I* did. It got out of hand. I said hello to one man fifteen times in two hours.

I went out to the turntable shanty—and that's where Mr. Pickering was. He stared, desolated, at the yard engine. I didn't have to tell him. He *knew.*

"The poor little thing," he said. "The poor, poor little thing . . ."

We stood around, not talking after that, because he had said it all.

Pretty soon Mr. Duveneck shadowboxed his way to where we were and said:

"Beershot, you ain't got the sense God gave a goose!"

"Let him be," I said.

Mr. Duveneck shadowboxed the Big Dipper.

"I thought there was a reason you was hanging around that engine so much," the hostler said. "So last night I looked her over good. Beershot, don't you realize they done put more main rods on her than she'll use in ten years?"

"Let him be," I said.

"Listen," Mr. Duveneck said. "I just had to talk to the first-trick foreman about her. Oh, don't worry, Beershot. I ain't no company man. I didn't tell him about you. He's got grief enough. But anyway, the second trick finished her up and—" he pointed to the locomotive "—there she sits!"

Mr. Pickering shuddered.

But he had never learned anger nor had he mastered rage.

"I guess," he said, dejected, "I'll go check the board and see what's scheduled for me tonight . . ."

"*Oh no you don't!*" the hostler cried. "You ain't going to leave me like this!"

"Like what?" said Mr. Pickering, not really caring.

Mr. Duveneck stopped shadowboxing.

"Suppose she dies?" he said.

"Suppose who dies?" I said. He wasn't making sense.

"The bird, *that's* who!" Mr. Duveneck said.

"But . . ." Mr. Pickering began.

Mr. Duveneck was furious.

"Somebody has got to feed her," he raved. "Last night I saw her in the tender. I knew the engine would be fired up before I could tell you, so I got her out of there. She could have been killed!"

Mr. Pickering came alive.

"The poor little thing is all right?" he asked, not daring to believe. His voice trembled with gladness.

"No!" Mr. Duveneck complained. "She's *not* all right. She's starving, that's what she is. And she won't eat no Wheaties! She must be crazy. Wheaties is the breakfast of champions. Wheaties is . . ."

"Where is she?" said Mr. Pickering.

34

"Up in my shanty. That's what I been trying to tell you, but nobody lets me get a word in edgewise. Beershot, you got to feed her. You got to . . ."

But he stopped talking. Mr. Pickering was gone. Mr. Pickering was hurrying to resume a love affair. Mr. Duveneck watched him go, turned, and said to me:

"Kid, how would you like a busted jaw?"

The anger in his voice surprised me.

"What did *I* do?" I said.

"Nothing," he said. "But if you don't want your jaw busted, that bird is between me and you and Beershot. Right?"

"Right!"

"And another thing: so is that angel junk. Understand?"

Mr. Duveneck looked at Mr. Pickering, already far up the track.

"If the other guys knew," he said, "they'd laugh."

And he shadowboxed away.

I stayed at the turntable. I was confused.

That's the trouble with being eighteen. Mr. Duveneck had me buffaloed. What can an eighteen-year-old Lit. Major do when a guy he wants to hate turns out to have compassion, too?

7

Kathleen didn't understand that the "Over the Rhine" district—Vine Street between Central Parkway and McMicken Avenue—was the climate Mr. Pickering needed. When we got off the streetcar at Twelfth and Vine, she looked nervous.

"Is this the neighborhood you meant?" she said.

"Yes," I said. "This is where Mr. Pickering feels America is."

"Oh," she said.

Her trouble was, she didn't know what kind of America Mr. Pickering had in mind. Mr. Pickering's America *was* outer Vine Street. Bars were everywhere and he had sampled every one. He knew which watered its whiskey and which didn't. He knew which put too much head on its beer. He knew where the hard-boiled eggs and pretzels were the freshest. He was the Duncan Hines of bars and he left nothing to chance. Each day he rechecked his findings. Each noon he began at McMicken and Vine Street and wet his whistle in each bar until it was ten that night. By then he had reached Central Parkway, he boarded a streetcar and came to work. The *important* thing, he informed me, was never to have a second drink in any bar. "I'd be off schedule," he said, "and late for work."

"Mr. Pickering told me about every bar on Vine Street," I told Kathleen as we stepped around a drunk. "He says

36

there is more folklore on Vine Street than on any other street in the world."

"He sounds nice," said Kathleen, and held my hand tighter.

She had good reason. The "Over the Rhine" district had become a shabby neighborhood. In the long-ago world of my grandpa, the district had been a happy area, good-natured and filled with malty joys. There had been signs that said: *A Free Wienerwurst with Every Drink.* Vine Street had been a noisy and respectable thoroughfare lined with beer gardens, concert halls, shooting galleries, and bowling alleys. Between Twelfth and Thirteenth streets had been twenty-three saloons. Vine Street had awed Carrie Nation. She didn't use her ax once. "I would have dropped dead from exhaustion," she had said, "before I had gone a block."

The "Over the Rhine" district had once been German. The "Rhine" had been the Miami and Erie Canal. It separated outer Vine Street from downtown Cincinnati. In 1940, it wasn't a canal. It had been filled in, paved, and called Central Parkway. But cross into outer Vine Street during my grandpa's time and you'd have been in a Teutonic world of German music and German cooking. There had been beer halls with singing waiters; and twenty-one steins of beer cost a dollar. Bars had sawdust on the floors and tanbark. And the food: steam dumplings, hasenpfeffer, potato pancakes, ham noodles, kidney soup, beef goulash, sauerbraten, and ham hocks with cornmeal dumplings. On side streets, each morning *old world* housewives had gotten on their knees and scrubbed each *old world* doorsill clean.

The district struggled back to life after Prohibition, but it couldn't recapture its yesterdays. The Germans, no longer laborers, had moved to the suburbs. Time chipped away at the German restaurants until only Gammer's, in the district, remained. It found itself a novelty on a street where it had once been commonplace. German bands oompahed

37

their final oompah and were replaced by a Tennessee tune. Vine Street dwindled into a dreary thoroughfare of secondhand stores and tired, little bars. Doorsills were no longer scrubbed. German was not the language; hillbilly was.

Twilight on Vine Street was the saddest hour. That was when Kathleen and I arrived. People leaned from third-floor windows and watched the action of the street. Children screamed at sidewalk games. The grinding noise of streetcars was constant and so was the dinging of their bells at each intersection. The music of the jukebox blended with the noise the streetcars made, and there was no quiet. The smell of bacon frying hung in the night air and so did the smell of sweat, beer, and the disinfectant the bars used. Vine Street had become a honky-tonk world filled with honky-tonk people.

If you must know, it was not *the* place to take Kathleen, but where else could she meet Mr. Pickering? Besides, I had no right to be uppity. Sedamsville was no better. Vine Street, at least, had history. Sedamsville had only the railroad.

Kathleen looked around.

"Where are we meeting Mr. Pickering?" she said.

"He'll be drinking down the west side of the street," I said.

"The *west* side?"

"There are too many bars, Kathleen. One day he drinks down one side and the next day, down the other."

"Do you mean," she said, "he's out there somewhere, *drinking* toward us?"

I said yes.

"How will we find him?" she said.

"Easy," I said. "We start at *this* end. We have one beer in each bar. We drink toward him. He drinks toward us. And we meet."

"Provided," Kathleen said, "we can still *see* him."

We walked into the first bar, sat at a table, ordered two bottles of Burger, and clinked them together in a toast.

"Cheers," said Kathleen with resignation. Then she grinned—and made the world right. I got the biggest kick out of her. The craziest things made her glad: watching puppies in pet shop windows, poking along kicking at leaves, sniffing bread in bakeries, and sometimes the idea of me. She was a slim beauty, had the mystery of a woman, and could ride a bicycle—no hands—with the vengeance of a child. She was an easygoing girl with hair that bounced around her shoulders; she could disarm anyone with a grin; when asked, she could imitate a hoot owl; but she wasn't a Pollyanna and she wasn't always sunny. When her younger brother read her diary, she seethed. When a guy in school tried to kiss her, she slugged him. Certain songs on the radio made her sad. And when she played the piano, she got misty. She belonged to everything shiny and new, but the bar we were in was run down, faded, and old. It was filled with people who drank beer and dreamed hand-me-down dreams.

All ages and shapes of men in shirt sleeves had watched Kathleen enter. Then, elbows still on the bar, they turned back to their beers and forgot her. They weren't gangsters. They weren't sex maniacs. They were truck drivers, bread-route men, freight handlers, and janitors. Some were bald. Some had hair. Some had muscle. Some had flab. They drank, ate beer nuts, smoked cigarettes, and argued about cat fishing, the Cincinnati Reds, and the Democratic convention in Chicago. Mostly they were from Kentucky, Tennessee, and West Virginia. They had a pride so fierce it kept them free of the law. They had to talk loud; the jukebox was louder.

Other than the jukebox that stunned us with its wild colors, the only decorations in the bar were signs that advertised beer and whiskey. These signs bubbled, twirled, glowed, bounced, jiggled, and wiggled—or simply dangled and did nothing but gather dust. The bar was well lighted, reasonably clean, and smelled of Burger beer, popcorn, and Airwick. One door said *Ladies*. Another said *Gents*. The bartender needed a shave, the waitress called most of her customers honey, and there were seven tables in the bar.

At one, a sweating fat man in an undershirt and work pants was arguing with a sweating fat lady in a housedress. They argued about buying a car. He wanted to. She didn't. I heard him say, "Why are you giving me grief? I get grief enough from my wife!" Then they argued about that. They didn't get violent. They just got loud, sweated some more, and ordered more beer.

At another table were two couples our age, but they looked married. The fellows wore bib overalls—clean—and white shirts—clean—buttoned at the collar and no ties. The girls wore skirts and blouses. They didn't talk. They sat and listened to the hillbilly tune the jukebox played. One girl held a baby in her arms. The baby was asleep. Now and then she would look down and smile a beautiful smile at it.

At the table in back, sitting alone, was a wrinkled old man. He was at least eighty years old. He was carrying on a conversation with the wall calendar.

I suppose if a fellow was looking for trouble out Vine Street he could find it fast, but who wanted it? The night was too hot. All most wanted was a cold beer. Even on Saturday nights when men had payday money to spend, Vine Street wasn't an angry street. Nobody went around starting fights. Nobody hit his wife. They saved that kind of stuff, as everyone else does, until they got home. Besides, the Cincinnati police could be stern. They patrolled outer Vine Street in pairs. They said hello, were amiable enough, but they also twirled their nightsticks, which reminded people nightsticks were to hit with.

Well, after we drank one beer, we moved to the next bar. Darkness made the neighborhood a little better. All we saw was neon. All we heard was noise: jukeboxes, children, and streetcars. Night made everything above the storefronts disappear. Across the street was a chili parlor. The smell of onions, chili beans, cheese, coffee, and grease drifted out its front door or was hurled into the night by the fan over the door. Kathleen and I paused at a novelty shop window. It was filled with plaster-of-paris Statues of Liberties, each with a clock in its belly. Kathleen laughed.

"Don't laugh," I kidded. "I'm getting you one for your birthday."

"If you do," she said, "I'll belt you."

The next bar, except for different customers, could have been the first.

"I didn't know places like this existed," Kathleen said.

I didn't say anything. I had known such places all my life.

"I like it," Kathleen said. She touched my hand. "The people seem nice."

"Shut up and drink your beer," I said, joking, of course.

"Cheers," she said.

We sipped. Then we waited. In this bar, or the next, we would meet Mr. Pickering. He would be surprised. What I mean is, he wasn't expecting us. He had said no to the idea.

"She don't want to meet me," he had protested. "Take her to a movie."

Mr. Pickering and I had been killing time at 4 A.M. and I had shocked him by announcing:

"Kathleen wants to meet you. I told her about you."

He had looked to see if I was making fun of him; I wasn't.

"Why'd you go and tell her things?" he said. "I'm not the kind of bird guys introduce their women to. Listen, I was walking along River Road the other day, feeling no pain, and along comes this machinist with his little girl. No more'n five. You know—young. Well, he up and crossed to the other side of the street. He pretended he hadn't seen me, but he had. I didn't blame him. I had a snootful and he was with his little girl . . ."

He had watched a yard engine chug to the ashpit.

"No, you listen here," he had said. "Tell your girl I'm busy. Okay? But tell her nice. Don't hurt her feelings. She's a nice girl."

"How do you know? You've never met her."

41

"I've met *you*," he had said.

When I told Kathleen this, she got tears in her eyes.

"Now I want to meet him more than ever," she said.

"But he said . . ."

She shook her head. She could be obstinate.

"I *want* to," she said.

"But why?"

"Because," she explained.

And so there we were in the Vine Street bar waiting to give Mr. Pickering the surprise of his life.

And there was Mr. Pickering at the door.

8

"Mr. Pickering! Over here!"

Mr. Pickering blinked at the sound of his name.

"Uh . . . uh . . ." he muttered. Adrift on a sea of doubt and drink, he stood in the doorway. He was bewildered and mystified. He didn't know which way to look first. He had never been paged on Vine Street before—by his family name. He stood in the door, his soul flooded with indecision. He was befuddled, confounded, and lost. He repeated:

"Uh . . . uh . . ."

"Over *here*, Mr. Pickering," I called. "It's me. It's *George*."

"Is he all right?" said Kathleen.

"He's three sheets to the wind."

"What?"

"He's drunk."

"Oh."

"*Over here, Mr. Pickering!*"

Our eyes met. His were glassy, but there was vague recognition in them. Carefully he moved across the bar and stopped in front of our table.

"I didn't know you in *street* clothes," he said. "I never saw you in street clothes before."

He looked around, determined which bar he was in, and added:

"Watch out for the pretzels here."

He stood before us: a seedy and dilapidated man of no

43

consequence; a lost-in-the-crowd kind of man who drooped and was dull. The world had battered him, rendered him bland, and tailored him threadbare. In the roundhouse, wearing overalls, Mr. Pickering possessed a majesty. His street clothes took the majesty away. He wore blue trousers. They bagged at the knees. They bagged at the bottom. His sport shirt—splashed with yellow flowers that fought one another—was basically red. It did not hide his pot belly. It was the kind of shirt that looks dramatic in the store window; put it on and the drama goes away. He wore a panama hat, which, when he approached, he removed. His head was bald. It glistened with skin.

Well, there he teetered: drunk and unsure of himself, his bald head glistening. He didn't know whether to sit, stand, or leave. He didn't know what words to say. He stood: becalmed and sweating.

"Mr. Pickering," I said. "I'd like to present Kathleen."

"Kathleen?"

"My *girl*."

"Oh," he said—and blushed.

Kathleen stepped in. "I've heard so much about you, Mr. Pickering. George talks about you all the time. He . . ."

"George?"

"*Me*," I said.

"But I call you the kid."

"Well, my name is George."

"Why do I call you the kid?"

"It doesn't matter, Mr. Pickering," I said.

"George says you're the best machinist in the roundhouse. He . . ."

"George?"

"*Me!*"

"You're *George?*"

"Forget it," I said.

"No," he said. "I'll call you George."

We were getting nowhere. Mr. Pickering was standing.

Kathleen was smiling. And I was confused. So I stood up and said:

"Mr. Pickering, what'll you have? I'm buying."

He became alive. "A-shot-and-a-beer," he said with authority. But, in a twinkling, his authority vanished. He became flustered. "No, no," he said. "*I'll* buy. Wait . . ."

We watched him drift to the bar. Kathleen, her elbows on the table, her chin cupped in her hands, studied him with her solemn, brown eyes. I couldn't tell what she was thinking. Probably she was fed up with the evening. It wasn't, I realized, as glorious as I had anticipated.

"Well," I said, "that's Mr. Pickering. But he takes a lot of knowing before you really know him. He . . ."

". . . is everything you said he was."

"Don't kid," I said to her. "He's a nice guy. He's . . ."

"I'm *not* kidding," she said. She grinned as she watched him trying to attract the bartender's notice. "He *is* what you said. And he likes you, George. He likes you a lot."

I felt better. She felt what I had felt.

"Well, yes," I said, relaxing. "But men don't talk about stuff like that. They . . ."

"I know *you* don't," she said. I had never seen her eyes so frank.

She flustered me.

"What do you mean by that?" I said.

She looked back at Mr. Pickering. He had finally gotten the bartender's attention.

"Nothing," she murmured. Her voice was distant.

"You're upset about something!"

She didn't take her eyes from Mr. Pickering. "No," she said. "It's just that you're the world's greatest dope. You need a ton of bricks to fall on you before . . . shhhh. Here comes Mr. Pickering."

"You're angry," I said.

"No, George," she said. "I'm not angry. Now hush."

Mr. Pickering drifted back to us. He carried a tray. On it were two bottles of Burger beer for us, and for himself: a

45

glass of beer and a shot of whiskey. He avoided people with great care. He gave everyone wide berth. He didn't want to dribble a drop.

Safety First was the roundhouse motto and it was his, too. Slowly, slowly, he set the tray on the table. With caution, he distributed the drinks and—in slow motion—sat. Sitting, he realized, can jar a table and jarring a table can spill drinks. Fingering his shot of whiskey, he looked at us and said:

"Cheers."

Without waiting, he raised his whiskey; his hand trembled, but not a drop spilled. In one gulp he drained the shot glass, found solace in it, and washed the solace down with beer. He leaned back, said *ah,* felt better, and peered at Kathleen.

"Say," he said, "what pretty eyes you got."

"Thank you, Mr. Pickering."

"You got that from the kid, didn't you? Calling me *Mr. Pickering.* Everybody else calls me . . ."

"I'd like to call you Mr. Pickering," Kathleen said. "May I?"

She smiled, reached some secret place inside him, and the niceness of her smile distressed him. When he answered, he spoke in a muted voice.

"That would be nice," he said. He looked at her carefully. "Have you been sick or something?"

She shook her head no.

"You ought to eat more," he said. "You're nothing but skin and . . ."

"Have some beer," I said, fast. I poured beer into his glass. And to make sure the subject was changed, I said, "Did we surprise you?"

"*Surprise* me?" he said, lost.

"Seeing us here, I mean," I said.

"Uh . . . uh . . ."

He was speechless.

It dawned on him: the meeting had been no accident. He drank his beer to have time to organize his embarrassment.

46

"And I told you not to," he said at last. "I told you . . ."
He stopped. He couldn't go on. That we had—deliberately
—set out to meet him was too beautiful to digest.
"Let me get more beer for us," he said. I had never seen
him so touched.
"But I still have half a . . ." Kathleen started to say, but
she stopped. "Yes," she said. "That would be nice."
He walked to the bar faster and with more assurance.
When he returned, he said:
"I would have put on a nicer shirt and wore a tie if I had
known. But I told the kid not to bring you."
"I made him do it," Kathleen said. "Don't be angry with
George."
"George?"
"*Me.*"
"Oh. No, kid, I couldn't be angry with you. I'm more sur-
prised than anything. One time there was this machinist
walking his little girl and . . ."
"Cheers, Mr. Pickering," I said. "Drink up!" I said it fast.
"Yes," he said. He drank and looked at Kathleen. "So
you're George," he said to her.
A silence came to our table. Mr. Pickering stared into his
glass so long I thought he had dozed off. But he hadn't. He
was untangling an idea he didn't know how to express. Fi-
nally, when the silence became almost too much, he looked
up and said:
"Kid."
"Yes?"
"You got to get out of the roundhouse."
He didn't say it with anger, but he said it, and I was
stunned. I thought he liked me.
Kathleen was stunned, too.
"Listen," I said. "I *have* to work, and the roundhouse pays
good, and . . ."
". . . You *got* to get out of the roundhouse," he repeated,
as if I had not said a word.
Kathleen dived in.

47

"He will, Mr. Pickering. But in a little while . . ."

He waved hands at us and stopped us both.

"Don't you see?" he said, his voice troubled. "There's no such thing as 'a little while.' Pretty soon a year is shot. And pretty soon a bunch of them." He looked at Kathleen. The desperation in his eyes was a blend of love and booze. "No, there's more to the kid than that. You got to make him get out of there."

"But, Mr. Pickering . . ." I said.

I didn't have to go on. The war was over. Mr. Pickering had stopped, appalled at the strength of his utterances—and with that, his strength went down the drain.

"I don't know what came over me, kid," he said, abashed. "Tell her I don't usually go around being a smart aleck. Tell her I don't usually . . ."

"He doesn't have to tell me, Mr. Pickering," said Kathleen. Her voice was sad. "I know you don't."

"You do?"

"Yes," she said.

He struggled to his feet.

"I'll be right back," he blurted—and hurried out the front door.

I was confused. I hadn't realized he *cared* about me. The last man who cared had been my father.

From far away, I heard Kathleen's troubled voice:

"Will he come back?"

"I don't know," I said. "Kathleen, did you *hear* what he said about me? Did you hear . . ."

"He loves you," she said and squeezed my hand. "But he doesn't know the words. That's the trouble with men."

"The beer is reaching you," I said. The mood was too stunning. I had to end it.

"Maybe," she said. She refused to let the mood go. "But I'm glad I met him."

"So am I," I said. "He . . . *no!*"

Mr. Pickering had returned. In his arms was a plaster-of-paris Statue of Liberty. The clock in its belly was ticking. Carefully he placed it in front of Kathleen.

"It's a present," he said. "I wanted you to have something nice."

I looked at Kathleen. She looked at me. Then she looked at Mr. Pickering.

"It's beautiful," she said. "You shouldn't have."

She tried not to look at it.

"They had smaller ones," said Mr. Pickering. "But I got you the biggest they had. It's a clock, too."

"It's what I've always wanted," Kathleen said.

Tell me: how can girls smile when they don't mean it?

Mr. Pickering didn't know how she felt; he was basking in the glow her smile made.

"I wanted you to have it," he said. "I owe you something."

"For what?"

"For sounding off about the kid. That wasn't nice of me. And for the way you surprised me tonight. Listen, I was never surprised like this before."

He worked his hands helplessly; they couldn't help him find the words.

"I've never had a lovelier gift," said Kathleen.

Mr. Pickering, still standing, said:

"You *will* get him out of the roundhouse, won't you?"

"I'll try," Kathleen said.

They exchanged looks that were pledges.

"I better go," he said. "I got one more bar before—well, did the kid tell you how I do? One drink in each bar. But I had two here. That puts me behind schedule. The kid is off tonight, but I ain't. I got to get to work. But you two have fun. You don't need a bird like me around. Good-by, kid. Get her to eat. Put some meat on her bones."

And he was gone.

Kathleen and I had another beer. We didn't joke about the statue that ticked. We hardly talked.

Pretty soon, though, she said:

"Let's go, George."

"Why?"

"Because I want to kiss you."

"What brought *that* on?" I said.

"If you're a good boy," she said, "someday I'll tell you."

9

If it wasn't his night off, it was mine, so I didn't see Mr. Pickering for three nights—and there was much we had to discuss: like, how I *had* to work because of my mother and for college, and had *he* ever kissed a girl who was holding a Statue of Liberty that ticked. Also, he was a nice guy; I simply wanted to see him again. But when I did, there was no time to talk of these items.

As I explained to Kathleen:

"It's no laughing matter. At least, not to me. Mr. Pickering and I could have been arrested!"

She nodded.

"And I'd have baked you both a cake and put a file in it," she said.

Sometimes she exasperated me.

"Don't frown," she said. "I think it's hilarious."

"It wasn't hilarious," I said. "It was eerie."

"The man actually tried to steal a locomotive?" she grinned. "He actually tried to take it home, piece at a time, in his lunch box? George, that's beautiful."

At times she was an unreal child. Her imagination was playful and wild. She could unravel gibberish and find sense in it.

"Kathleen," I said, "do you mind if I tell it the way it happened? And *not* the way Mr. Pickering *thought* it happened? The man wasn't trying to take a locomotive home in his

51

lunch box. That's Mr. Pickering's version. And it wasn't my idea to get the roundhouse blessed. That was Mr. Pickering's idea. All I wanted to do was explain to him why I had to work at the roundhouse, and the next thing I knew, he . . . Kathleen, will you please stop grinning?"

"Start at the beginning," she said. "And don't leave out a single thing. I wouldn't miss this for the world."

And she grinned some more.

Well, it was too hot to argue with her. Nora Ford, at the Cat & Fiddle nightclub on Central Avenue where salesmen went, was billed as "The Red-hot Redhead," but that July she wasn't alone. We all ran around with our tongues hanging out. Dog days smothered the city. Nights were scorchers. Sleep during the day was impossible. I'd get home from work, eat breakfast, listen to Glenn Miller records, try to sleep, lie in bed—and sweat. The electric fan gushed hot air only. I'd get up, prowl the house, drink ice water, and sweat some more. Once a week around three-thirty I'd walk to Eighth and State, go into the Paradise Ice Cream Parlor, and meet Kathleen. She would be coming from piano lessons, wait at Eighth and State for a streetcar to take her home, and while she waited, we'd sit in the Paradise and talk. That afternoon she wanted me to describe the events of the night before when the police came to the roundhouse, we got the roundhouse blessed, and—let me begin at the beginning.

The beginning was exactly midnight: fifteen and a half hours earlier. Mr. Pickering, Mr. Duveneck, and I—hoping for a breeze to come that never did—were sitting on the turntable. We dangled our feet, we sweated, and the railroad was quiet. Now and then, inside the roundhouse, an engine popped. Somewhere inside a machinist banged with a sledgehammer, but soon his banging stopped, and only silence remained.

Mr. Duveneck had just finished explaining how a heat wave is good for muscle tone, when the red light flashing on the police car attracted our attention. The police car, coming

52

onto railroad property, passed the powerhouse and disappeared from sight behind the roundhouse.

"Beershot," Mr. Duveneck said, "they're coming after you. I knew it would happen someday."

"Aw, she's too hot to kid," said Mr. Pickering with no bitterness. "They're probably lost."

"Police don't drive around lost," Mr. Duveneck said. "They know every street and alley in the third district."

"Suppose, though, they're from the second district—and lost?" Mr. Pickering said.

Mr. Duveneck was about to answer, but a commotion inside the roundhouse stopped him. Shouts of "Let me go!" and "We got you!" and "I dint do it!" and "Catch him! He got away!" filled the air. We watched two policemen chase Mr. Hoover, the third-trick pipe fitter. They chased him out of the roundhouse and into the turntable area's dark. Unused to rails, the policemen stumbled a lot, but the chase ended ten feet from where we sat. Mr. Hoover was stopped with a flying tackle.

"I dint do it!" Mr. Hoover cried. In desperation, he looked around and saw us. "Beershot, I dint do it!"

But the policemen carted him away and that was that.

"Of course he didn't do it," Mr. Pickering said.

"Didn't do *what?*" said Mr. Duveneck, perplexed.

"I don't know," Mr. Pickering said. "But you heard him say he didn't, didn't you? Why would he do a thing like that? He's got three kids."

"Why wouldn't he do a thing like *what?*" Mr. Duveneck demanded.

"Like what they arrested him for."

Mr. Duveneck began to drum his fingers.

"Cops," he said with great patience, "don't arrest people for the fun of it. They don't work on commission. They get paid even if they arrest nobody. It ain't like piecework. No, Hoover is as guilty as they come. He did it all right."

"Did what?" I said.

53

"Kid," said Mr. Pickering, "there is some things you ain't old enough to understand."

"Why don't we ask the foreman what happened?" I said.

"Well," said Mr. Pickering, "we might as well. Maybe she's cooler in there."

We learned that Mr. Hoover had been arrested for stealing railroad property: namely, brass. The foreman said the police had been watching him a long time. Each morning, when he left the roundhouse to go home, Mr. Hoover would sneak pieces of brass into his empty lunch box, take them home, and when he had enough piled up, he would sell them to a junkyard. The way the war was going in Europe, brass was at a premium; Mr. Hoover was cashing the premiums in.

"They searched his basement tonight after he came to work," the foreman said. "He's got more brass there than we got here."

"But he's got three kids," said Mr. Pickering, crestfallen.

"He almost had the New York Central railroad, too," the foreman said, went into his office, and closed the door. The foreman was sad and with good reason.

Railroad men belong to a private club called the railroad. The club isn't the greatest, has little to recommend it: it breaks your back, gives you gray hair, and makes you old before your time. Club members are forever muttering how awful the railroad is, how they can't wait to take their pensions, and how—when they do—they never want to see a railroad again. They're fed up with the funny hours, the weather the railroad shovels at them, and the way the railroad doesn't care if they live or die. The railroad costs some of them their arms, takes a lot of their fingers, scalds them if they're not careful, and drops heavy things on their toes. But two things keep the club members loyal: one, railroading is a love affair for men only; and two, the pay is good. The members are clannish, have little but cinders and stars in their eyes, plus their pride. But a member who steals takes that pride away. It is one thing, they agree, to hate the rail-

54

road, but to steal from it is not playing the game. I could sense the shock and disbelief in the foreman and the rest. But they didn't question that it happened. It had happened and had made them sad.

Well, that's not one hundred percent correct. Mr. Pickering questioned it.

He and I walked through the roundhouse, passed silent engines with a machinist sleeping in each cab, and he was troubled.

"I've known that bird eight years," he said. "He's got three kids. He wasn't stealing. What he was doing, was doing something for his kids." Mr. Pickering sighed, filled the air with Old Grand-Dad fumes, and said, "What he was *really* doing was taking pieces of an engine home so he could build his kids a railroad in their backyard."

I couldn't believe that.

"All he took was brass," I said.

"You got to start somewhere," Mr. Pickering said.

"Mr. Pickering, if he was making an engine for his kids, how was he going to get the driver wheels home? They'd never fit in his lunch box. And what about the main rods? And . . ."

"Eight years," Mr. Pickering explained, "is a long time to know a bird."

"And what about the boiler tubes?"

Mr. Pickering, badgered, looked at me with sadness.

"What about boiler tubes?" he said.

"How can a guy sneak those long things out of the roundhouse without being seen?"

"There you are," he yawned. "That proves it."

"Proves what?"

"That he wasn't stealing. Now, if he had took boiler tubes, *that* would be stealing."

"But he took brass."

"To build his kids a backyard railroad," Mr. Pickering said.

I was confused.

55

"What *kind* of engine was he going to build for them?"

"I guess she was going to be a Hudson," Mr. Pickering said. "He took brass that goes on a Hudson."

"He took brass for a Pacific, too," I said.

"Some guys," he said, "just don't know how to make toys for kids."

"Mr. Pickering, the cops say he *confessed* he was stealing."

"Confessed?"

"To the cops, Mr. Pickering."

He fumbled with this thought. It left him stricken. He blew his nose with a great honking noise and said:

"Them poor little kids. Them poor, poor little things . . ."

He stopped at a window and stared out at the night. Sadness—momentarily—had replaced hope that sloshed around the deeper levels of his being. A man who would not rock a boat, he was surrounded by those who would. He chewed his lower lip, looked out at the night, and for the longest time just stood.

"You okay, Mr. Pickering?"

"God is mad at railroads for some reason," he said. "Them poor, poor things . . ."

He looked at me as if I were a stranger.

"The trouble is," he said, "God ain't here."

"Here?"

"In the roundhouse. I'll bet He ain't been here in years."

"Mr. Pickering . . ."

"We got to get God back here before more kids get their hearts busted."

"Mr. Pickering, I'm not sure that's the reason . . ."

"There's got to be a way to get God looking out for the New York Central."

"But . . ."

"Or," he said, "would you rather have Him keep an eye on the B&O?"

"You're the boss," I said.

After all, he did know a lot about religious things.

Dulled by booze and awed by Christ, Mr. Pickering had

56

the vague feeling that Christ died for everybody but him. He never quarreled with Christ about this; he simply did not consider himself the sort of person that people got nailed to crosses for. That's one reason he stopped going to church. Another reason had been, he invariably got seated next to a child who kicked him during prayers. Mr. Pickering, fond of children, never blamed the child; but one Sunday when a minister announced, "A little child shall lead them," Mr. Pickering got frightened and stopped going to church.

Before he gave up churchgoing, he had tried them all. For a while he was a Baptist. Then he attended a Christian Reformed church. After that: the Church of Christ, the Church of the Nazarene, the Evangelical United Brethren church, the Greek Orthodox church, the Independent Fundamentalists, and the Latter Day Saints. He sampled the Lutherans, tested the Methodists, and, for a chaser, three Sundays in a row attended a Presbyterian church. Although he liked what he saw at a Jewish synagogue, he felt it wasn't for him; a Roman Catholic church bewildered him because he didn't understand the priest; the Salvation Army was more to his liking—they seemed a cheerful bunch—but the drumming made his head ache; the Unitarians were nice to him, and so was the flock at the Church of Truth. The Pillar of Fire, Jehovah's Witnesses, and God's Bible School did their best to make him feel welcome, but he never did; and he attended the *I Am* sanctuary only once; they were, but he wasn't.

All of this background found its way through the Old Grand-Dad mist in his soul, however, and gave him an idea.

"They bless cars, don't they?" he said. "Well, we got to get the roundhouse blessed. You seen it, ain't you? Down there at St. Vincent De Paul's church on River Road where automobiles get blessed? They got this statue of St. Christopher holding the baby Jesus on his shoulder, the poor little thing, and . . ."

"But how are you going to get a roundhouse blessed?"

"I read where they put her up in 1928. The first of July. I

remember because that same day Obregón was reelected president of Mexico. Of course, they assassinated him sixteen days later, but that's where cars is blessed, so why not roundhouses, too? God keeps an eye on everything, don't He?"

"But *how* are you going to get the roundhouse blessed?"

"She won't be easy," he said. "Come on."

Ten minutes later, her load of empty fire buckets rattling loud enough to wake the dead, the green electric crane—guided by Mr. Pickering—bounced out the roundhouse door and into the hot, dark night outside. I sat on the crane's front platform; my job: to keep the buckets from falling off. The crane had no headlights, but Mr. Pickering knew the way. He steered the crane along the powerhouse road; soon the powerhouse was behind us, and there was River Road. No traffic moved. It was too late at night.

Without hesitation Mr. Pickering ran the crane out into the street, aimed it west, and—with crashes and bangs and bumpity bumps—we headed to St. Vincent De Paul, two miles west. The crane was railroad property, had no license plates, had no lights, had never been outside of the roundhouse before, and you get the idea. You can see why, as we rode along, I worried a lot.

The roundhouse had not one, but two electric cranes. When not humming through the roundhouse with a main rod swinging from their hooks, they nested by the toolroom and sucked fresh electric power from a wall plug to recharge their batteries for another go at railroading. They were, in a way, electric automobiles without beauty and charm. On the front was the crane, in the middle was the battery box—enormous and heavy—and on the back was a one-step platform where the operator stood, steered, and worked the controls. They couldn't move through the house fast. Their top speed was fifteen miles an hour. On the first trick, a full-time crane operator ran one of them. He had mastered the gadgets. On the second trick everyone ran the crane. It didn't matter whether they had mastered the beasts or not.

On the third trick we used the crane so seldom, none of us mastered the things, but that didn't stop us from playing with them. There was little else to do, the cranes were sturdy items, and we didn't run anyone down with them. Now and then we bounced one into an empty engine pit, but retrieving it was duck soup: we used the other crane.

The cranes were needed. Main rods were too heavy to carry; and though the men were strong, none had the strength to pull the boiler tubes out of the front of the engines—and they were forever doing that. The railroad pampered its locomotives. Since the heart of a steam locomotive was its boiler, they pampered the boiler most. Cranes came in handy for that kind of pampering.

Once a month—or sooner, if the engine seemed tired and run down—a locomotive would be pulled out of service, its fire banked, and run into the roundhouse, where boiler washers washed its boiler. Once every *three* months the engine would, besides having its boiler washed, be run through a "train stop" test. A machinist would check its air gauges, pumps, and stuff. Once every *six* months, the engine would not only have its boiler washed and its gauges dusted, it would have its brakes looked at and its valves changed. Once every *twelve* months, all this would happen, and—in addition—to see how sick the engine really was, the railroad would run a hydrostatic test of its boiler. They'd fill the boiler, all its pipework and connections, with water instead of steam. They'd put the water under great pressure, then stand back and watch. Where water squirted out, that's where steam would have leaked out, too. They'd study the engine that was squirting water at them, feel sad, and pretty soon they'd drain the water, patch the leaks, send the locomotive back into service, and cross their fingers. Each of these monthly tests was called a "card." Don't ask me why. All I know is, the way the engines were constantly being yanked out of service and tested, I wondered if the New York Central had enough engines left to pull the trains. I'm glad that wasn't my problem. Anyway, there always

59

seemed to be enough engines and then some, but still, they went in and out of service a lot. Every twenty-four hours at least forty engines chugged into the roundhouse to be annointed with coal, water, grease, and steam.

Well, when Mr. Pickering and I arrived at the church, the night was dark and silent. No one had seen us.

There was really only one street: River Road, which was U.S. 50 and took you to Indiana. That night no one wanted to go, so no cars or trucks traveled it. I'm glad they didn't.

If the rattling of the buckets awakened anyone—the night was a scorcher and every window in every house was open —they would have looked out their windows and not believed their eyes. In turn, they would have awakened their wives, or their husbands, whichever was the case, and said: "Is it possible to get sunstroke from the moon?"

The point is, and I've exaggerated a little to put it across because nobody would have said a thing like that, no one saw us and I'm glad. You know what I mean.

We did have one scare, though.

From the roundhouse west, the streetcar tracks didn't travel along the street. They ran on their own private right-of-way between the street and the railroad tracks. Owl cars, with no traffic to watch out for, bucketed through the night ignoring everything, sometimes even ignoring people waiting to get on, because the motorman was a dreamer and to him night was for dreaming things. Besides, he knew his regular riders. Those he didn't, he passed by. He thought they might be burglars. The reason I tell you this is the streetcar passed us that night. For one brief moment we were lighted by the streetcar's single headlight, but the motorman, his head bent and dreaming things, didn't look up, and soon the streetcar and its noise were swallowed up by the night. But, still, it was too close for comfort.

Mr. Pickering, woolgathering, ran the crane right by the church and didn't stop. If I hadn't mentioned this to him, we would have kept heading west and, unless the batteries pooped out, I might have been writing this from Colorado, Kansas, or someplace else.

"Oh," he said.

He made a U-turn in the middle of River Road and headed back to the church.

"When you been to a lot of them," he yawned, "they begin to look alike. Churches, I mean. Well, here we is."

St. Vincent De Paul church sits up and back from the road on a little hill. At street level a driveway swings off River Road, passes the statue of St. Christopher, and turns back onto River Road again. On Sundays, after the ten o'clock mass, and on Sunday afternoons at three, the priest stands by the statue and blesses the automobiles that pull in, which cars have been doing since they built the thing, and business was good.

Mr. Pickering stopped the crane in front of the statue and blinked at how awesome the statue was.

"Say, ain't she a sweet one, though," he said, impressed. "Take off your cap, kid. She's the same here as being in church. Show your respect."

"All right," I said. I removed my hat. "Now what?"

He scratched his chin.

"I was hoping there'd be a holy water pump around here," he said. "I thought we could get a couple of gallons, cart her back, and dribble her around the roundhouse. You don't see no faucet, do you?"

Railroad men always carry flashlights. We got ours out and searched around the statue. No faucet. But that made sense. Maybe the priest just blessed cars with words. Maybe he didn't sprinkle water on them. I'm not Catholic, as you can tell, and a lot they do is lost on me, but I had the feeling holy water didn't come out of a faucet. What I mean is, it was a place to get cars blessed; it wasn't a car wash.

"Well," said Mr. Pickering, bewildered, "we can let this Christopher bird bless the crane without water. Then we can take the crane back and kind of run her around the

61

roundhouse and say religious things. Suppose that would do?"

I didn't know. Blessing a roundhouse was not my line of work. I told him so.

He looked hurt.

"Aw, kid," he said. "Don't be that way. God likes roundhouses. If He hadn't, He would have denounced them."

"God," I said, "has more important things to do than denounce roundhouses."

"No," said Mr. Pickering. "It says in the Good Book that how can we go around cursing what God hasn't gotten around to cursing yet, and how can we denounce what God never bothered with denouncing. It didn't say it *exactly* that way. Them birds that write Bibles has a queer way of expressing themselves, but the thought is there, ain't it?"

"All right," I said. "Let's get the crane blessed and go back before we get into trouble."

"I guess we better," he sighed. He peered at St. Christopher. The statue, a lifesize Carrara marble work, ignored him. The statue was too busy keeping the stone baby Jesus from falling off his shoulder.

"But how do we know," said Mr. Pickering, "when that bird is done blessing the crane?"

I didn't know.

"Maybe," said Mr. Pickering, "we should say a prayer or something and get him thinking religious things."

Without waiting for an answer, he bowed his head.

"Now . . . uh . . . I lay me down to sleep, God," he mumbled—and made the moment lonely and beautiful.

Head bowed, hands folded, he was a monk in greasy overalls. He mumbled that long-ago prayer and did not doubt once that God was on the phone. It didn't occur to him to ask God's blessing for himself. God had more important things to bless. Adrift on a sea of Old Grand-Dad fumes, he was a fallen angel—lumpy, sleepy, and with a pot belly—who talked to God as men talk to men.

The conversation finished, he smiled a beery smile up at where God was, put his cap back on, and said:

"Well, I guess she's done."

"Let's get out of here fast," I said, but I said it gently.

He climbed up on the crane, waited for me to get on front, adjusted the controls, and we started along the curved driveway back to River Road. But we didn't get too far. The police car was blocking our path.

"Oh," said Mr. Pickering.

The policeman, who had coasted up without lights during Mr. Pickering's meditation, got out of the car and walked up to us. He was scratching his head in disbelief. You couldn't blame him much.

Mr. Pickering stopped the crane.

"Did you . . . uh . . . uh . . . come to get your police car blessed?" Mr. Pickering said. "You'll have to come back, though. God shut off the water."

"That's not the point," said the policeman. He looked confused. "The point is . . . the point is . . ."

He had difficulty putting the point into words.

"You're not trying to steal anything, are you?" he asked finally.

Mr. Pickering was shocked.

"She's too heavy to steal," he said, indicating the statue. Then he studied it again. "Well, we could hook a chain around her and . . ."

"We're not trying to steal anything!" I said, fast. "We're with the railroad and . . ."

"The railroad," said the policeman pointing to the tracks, "is there. This is the street. This . . ."

"Police cars," said Mr. Pickering, "should be blessed, too. Bring her by when this bird is open for business. You'll get a medal of St. Christopher and a good feeling. You'll . . ."

"Have *you* been drinking?" the policeman asked. He sounded irritated.

"Oh no," said Mr. Pickering, and tried to breathe the other way. "Never while I'm on duty."

"You're on duty? Where?"

"At the roundhouse. I'm a machinist . . ."

"*This* isn't the roundhouse," the policeman said. "This is St. Vincent De Paul church."

"She's a pretty one, too," said Mr. Pickering. "I went to her once. Where do you go to church?"

"That," said the policeman, "is not the point, either."

"No need to feel embarrassed," Mr. Pickering said. "They let anybody in here. They ain't proud."

The policeman stiffened.

"I don't think you should have said that," I said to Mr. Pickering.

He blinked at me. He was confused.

"But," he said, "nobody is proud in churches. They got humility there. And the wine they give is nice, too."

"I'm afraid," said the policeman, "I'm going to have to take you both in."

My heart sank.

"Well," said Mr. Pickering, "don't arrest the kid here. He didn't do nothing. He came along for the ride."

"Mr. Pickering," I said, "we're in this together."

"That's sweet of you," he said, "but you don't want to go to no prison. They're not nice."

"I've got to take you *both* in," the policeman said. "That's the way we do things."

"Oh," said Mr. Pickering. He searched his mind for cunning and found some. "Well, if that's the way she is, what are you arresting us for?"

"I'm charging you with . . . with . . ." The policeman looked pained. "I'll let the sergeant figure *that* out. There must be a bunch of things."

Mr. Pickering sighed and shook his head.

"No," he said. "There's a right way to do things. If you ain't going to say *why* we're arrested, we don't want to be arrested. They told Mr. Hoover tonight why he was arrested. We got the same rights."

64

"Well," said the policeman, "how's this for a start: disturbing the peace."

Mr. Pickering looked around the silent neighborhood. Every window was dark.

"We ain't disturbing nobody," he said. "What else you got?"

"Vagrancy?"

"We both got jobs."

We might have stood, arguing for hours, but Station X came on the air. That's the police radio station in Eden Park that broadcasts only to police cars. The announcer said somebody was breaking into a store near Eighth and State and suggested that somebody out there listening do something about it.

Tremendously relieved, the policeman ran to his car, shouting:

"You guys better be gone before I get back!"

And, *zoom!* Off he went.

I had the feeling he wasn't coming back ever.

"Well," said Mr. Pickering, "we better get back to the roundhouse."

"Weren't you worried?" I said.

He sighed.

"When a thing is blessed, what can go wrong?"

I didn't answer. How could I quarrel with Mr. Pickering? If a policeman couldn't, I wasn't about to try.

"And," Kathleen said, "that's *all* that happened. George, sometimes you worry too much."

"Whoever heard of blessing electric cranes?" I said.

"I see nothing wrong with that," she said. "When I was little I tried to get Daddy to take me there."

"Why?" I said.

"To get my roller skates blessed," she said.

Didn't I tell you she was an unreal child?

10

One afternoon it drizzled. By the time I walked through the railroad yards to work it was raining a rain in which yard engines—like lost trawlers—floundered. By the time I reached the dry of the roundhouse my socks were wet, my overalls were soaked, and the water that dripped off my chin depressed me.

At 1:30 A.M. Mr. Pickering said:

"Well, we is at least inside. Think of them that ain't."

"Like who?"

We were killing time in an engine cab.

"Like work trains," he said. He added: "Poor little things."

They *were* poor little things: the boxcars nobody wanted, the flatcars that had seen better days, and the passenger coaches whose youth had fled. Once single file, players in a thousand hotshot dramas, they had crisscrossed the nation, suffered the pain of hotboxes, the anguish of busted air hoses, and the embarrassment of the flat wheel's thump-thump-thump. But times changed and these older cars—swaybacked and unloved—were shunted onto a sidetrack and oblivion. They were sawed and hammered into bunk cars, tool cars, and rolling kitchens. Windows were hacked in their sides. Their doors were any doors the junkyard didn't want. Rickety stovepipe chimneys dotted their roofs.

"I'll bet you," said Mr. Pickering, "there is a hundred boxcars like that forgot somewhere on country turnouts."

He blew his nose with a honk.

"She ain't fit out for boxcar nor beast," he said. He added: "Or fat women, either. Here comes Rosalind."

Like something the cat dragged in, she trudged through the roundhouse, looking neither right nor left.

Bedraggled and dripping, she wore a man's hat that was black with wet and shapeless, a slicker that glistened with water and made her more of a colossus than she was, soaked gym shoes, and soggy anklets.

"You poor little thing," said Mr. Pickering. "What brings you out on such a terrible night?"

Drunk as seven hundred dollars, she said:

"Baby . . . baby . . . baby . . ."

Mr. Pickering and I hurried down from the engine cab to follow her.

She crossed from the deadhouse through the wild wet to the main part of the place. As she passed Hudsons and Pacifics, they sighed—because they were giants and lonely, too.

She permitted herself to be guided to where the sound of the rain was less and the lightning didn't flash: the blacksmith shop. I stood in its doorway and watched Mr. Pickering establish her on a sawhorse.

No blacksmiths worked the third trick. A single bulb lighted the anvil, forge, iron scraps, bellows, and coke. It was an eerie cave where the earth's diggings were heated, hammered, and reshaped to make a railroad run. Though the day's steam had been vented, its scent, lingering, mingled with the scent of dust, the dirt floor, sweat, and rust. The shop was filled with silence and gloom. The day's hisses and clangs had hissed and clanged and gone.

"You poor little thing," Mr. Pickering said.

Mr. Pickering could not console her. God had borrowed her baby and never brought it back. Did it cry at thunder? Did lightning make it tremble? Who would feed and water it?

"Baby . . . baby . . ."

Mrs. Bruce heard thunder, rain, and a baby's whimper.

Fat and forlorn she swayed and made the sawhorse creak in rhythm to the horrors she had. She was comfortless, filled with dejection, and depressed. She put on a long fat face, moaned the blues, and mumbled.

"Should we call a doctor?" I said.

"No. She needs to sleep it off."

"Where?"

"Here is cozy," said Mr. Pickering.

He took off his jumper and wrapped it around her shoulders.

"Rest," he said. "Me and the kid will leave you be."

We closed the door behind us. Once clear of the blacksmith area, Mr. Pickering looked pained and said:

"You know there ain't no baby, don't you?"

"I don't think," I said, "that the railroad likes using its roundhouse for . . ."

"Aw, don't be that way."

"But, Mr. Pickering, there *are* rules!"

"Let's see," he said and took from his pocket that little book with its stiff brown cover. He stared at the book with gloom. Only two and a quarter inches by five and three-quarter inches, it contained two dozen pages. Its title was *Safety Rules*. It was the railroad man's bible. It contained safety rules for everybody: engine, train, and yard employees; stationmen, linemen, and signal employees; track, bridge, and building employees; employees in electrified territory; and us: the shop employees. It had been written by the superintendent of safety. It had been approved by four vice-presidents and nine general foremen.

I approved, too. When you're reared in a railroad family, safety is all you know. Safety is drummed, every time they turn around, into railroad men. Big signs painted over doors say SAFETY FIRST. Big signs stenciled on walls say SAFETY FIRST. Other signs say ALWAYS BE CAREFUL; or if not much room: A-B-C; but the thought is the same. My father had forever shouted at me, "Always be careful!"

68

What the New York Central drummed into him, he tried to drum into me.

When I was young, my father let me read his safety rule book. It made railroading less exciting. For instance, Rule 4067 didn't allow men to kid.

Engine blowoff cocks must not be opened . . . where a person is near enough to be scalded.

Another rule fascinated me.

Stepping boxes must not be moved when passengers are about to step on them. Say to the passengers leaving car: "Watch your step."

I could see passengers stepping down from day coaches and the conductor, as he yanked the stepping box out from under them, shouting, "Watch your step!" When I asked my father if this happened much, he wouldn't let me read his safety rule book again.

"Never step on a rail," my father would say. "You'll slip and break your leg."

"Never jump off a moving train," he would say. "You'll land wrong and break your leg."

"Never play on a trestle. A train will hit you and break your leg."

"Look both ways before crossing the tracks."

"Stay out of boxcars."

"Don't step on frogs."

And, always, he added that if I didn't obey, I would break my leg. I broke my collarbone instead, which is a different story, and my father considered me a failure.

Mr. Duveneck, the hostler, on the other hand, had no time for safety rules.

"Clean living!" he said. "*That's* the only rule! And eat raw carrots."

"The book says nothing about that," I said.

"If *I* followed the book," he said, flexing his muscles, "the railroad would stop running."

"It would?"
"Look at Rule 4013."
I did.

Material must not be piled so it will fall.

"It sounds like a nice rule to me," I said.
"The coal dock," he said, "holds five hundred tons of coal."
"But what has that to do with . . ."
"Kid, don't you know nothing? Engines run under the coal dock and coal *falls* into their tenders. *Gravity*," he added, relishing the sound the word made. "That's the way gravity does. Never fails."
"But what has that to do with . . ."
"Kid, the rule says material mustn't be allowed to fall. Well, coal has to fall. Otherwise, why have a coal dock?"
"I don't think that's what they meant."
"They should say what they mean," said Mr. Duveneck—and ended the conversation with a headstand.

During my first week on the railroad, Mr. Martin, the first-trick turntable operator, had explained to me about the "Rule of the Week." It was not, he said, that he believed in such nonsense, but the roundhouse officials did, and officials had to be humored.

"The gang foreman will come around," he said, "and ask what the 'Rule of the Week' is. We're supposed to recite it, word for word. It gives the foreman something to do and makes him feel important."

The "Rule of the Week" was posted on the bulletin board in advance of the foreman's query, he said.

"If I don't have the rule memorized," I said, "will I be fired?"

"Foremen are slobs," he said. "They don't know beans."
He explained what he did. When the foreman asked Mr. Martin, Mr. Martin would look angry, take out his false teeth, and gum:

Stationmen must, after trucks are loaded or unloaded, immediately remove the goddamn things to safe clearance from

70

side of train. Power propelled trucks should be operated from the goddamn forward end and hand trucks pulled instead of pushed where practical, so help me God, wherewith, thereof, and safety first.

That rule—well, almost that rule—was a safety rule, but it had to do with stationmen only. However, as Mr. Martin pointed out, it had a familiar ring. It satisfied the foremen. Anyway, it was the only rule he had memorized. Lots of others did the same, he said, but a few had trouble because they had their teeth.

"It would help, kid, to get your teeth pulled," he said.

I decided it would be easier to memorize the "Rule of the Week" but I had, when I did, the uneasy feeling I was the only one.

Anyway, Mr. Pickering looked with reluctance at the rule book.

"There is a lot of swell rules here," he said, "but no rule says ladies can't sleep off their horrors in the blacksmith shop. In a boxcar is another matter. And so is the yardmaster's office. The yardmaster is hard-nosed. He wouldn't let me keep a goat there once."

I didn't feel like asking why Mr. Pickering wanted to keep a goat in the yardmaster's office. I decided to change the subject.

"Mr. Pickering, when will you and Mrs. Bruce be married? Have you ever asked her?"

"Not yet, kid. She's touchy. But we sweet talk though."

"Yes, but . . ."

"The day will come, kid."

"And meantime?"

"Well, I think how nice things will be: me and her in a love nest, drinking beer and smoochin'."

I had to say what troubled me.

"But she cusses all the time. She's mean. She'll never say a kind word to you. Mr. Pickering, there's nothing but hurt to her."

He peered at me.

71

"No, kid, it ain't that way," he said. His voice was troubled. "If there was only hurt in her, I wouldn't give her the time of day. A man wants more than that. What she needs is taming."

"Taming?"

He nodded.

"We is all wild birds before we is tamed. Wasn't we savages in caves, saying ugh and hitting with sticks? But we got amenities. And we changed. Well, so will Rosalind. It's a matter of taming."

"How do you tame a fat woman?"

"I don't know, kid. But it's worth figuring out. The prize is a whopper."

"Will you use a chair and whip, like lion tamers do?"

"No. If I use anything, I'll use kindness."

"And if that doesn't work, Mr. Pickering?"

"I'll back off and try again."

The rain stopped at 4:30 A.M. Operating the turntable, I had gotten soaked. But Mr. Duveneck, as he accepted whatever nature dished out, accepted rain. During the night I saw him with his head tipped skyward and his mouth open wide. "*This* is the stuff to drink," he shouted, "not tap water. Once a guy from the waterworks told me what they add to drinking water. No wonder the Nazis are supermen. *Rain water!*"

"Where did you hear that?" I said.

"They don't get water from the Cincinnati Waterworks, do they?" he answered.

I would have argued but it's impossible to argue with a man when it's raining in his mouth.

Dawn came slowly. The clouds were beginning to lighten when I saw Mrs. Bruce emerge from the roundhouse. Her face was a study in hate.

Mr. Pickering, the constant lover, bumbled a few steps in her wake.

"Kid," she sneered, "was you a party to what happened?"

It took her time to say it. Rain had not diluted her de-

72

scriptives, if you know what I mean. It took me time to sort out the nonessentials to get the gist. She was practically frothing at the mouth.

A translation of her next comment would be:

"Beershot enticed me into the blacksmith shop and toyed with my affections."

Mr. Pickering, standing on one foot and then the other, wishing he was dead, said:

"Uh . . . uh . . . uh . . ."

"I don't mind doing it in boxcars," she yapped.

"Uh . . . uh . . . uh . . ."

"And hammocks is fun."

"Uh . . . uh . . . uh . . ."

Although she mentioned five other locations—one of which surprised me—she expressed reluctance for blacksmith shops because she said a girl could get hurt on the anvil.

"Nothing *happened* in the blacksmith shop," Mr. Pickering pleaded.

"Then why entice me there?" she bellowed.

"I didn't. You had a snootful and . . ."

She stopped him with a comment which has nothing to do with the story.

"Mrs. Bruce," I said, trying to brighten the gathering, "when you and Mr. Pickering get married, things will be nicer."

"Me marry him?" she hooted.

"Kid," said Mr. Pickering, crushed, "I wish you hadn't said that."

He stopped. She towered over him and, had her stomach not interfered, would have pressed her nose against his.

"You terrible old something-or-other," she brayed. "You give me sick headaches."

They made a curious tableau. Mrs. Bruce and Mr. Pickering. Which was the beach and which was the tide? Which was the destroyer and which the destroyed? Mrs. Bruce was too angry to say more and Mr. Pickering was too shattered.

73

11

August became September; October came along and the
Cincinnati Reds won the pennant, Tom Mix died, Wendell
Willkie held a rally at Crosley Field, and Valerie Parks—
called "the hottest thing since the Chicago fire"—finished
her turn at the burlesque house. By October, Clyde McCoy
departed from the Beverly Hills nightclub, but Deanna Dur-
bin was still on the screen in *Spring Parade*. My point is,
the world moved on, but Mr. Pickering's love life had hit
dead center.

"I don't see how he can like Mrs. Bruce," I told Kathleen.
"I don't understand love."

"I know," said Kathleen—and picked one chord on the
organ, playing it soft.

She tried another chord and filled the church with a rum-
ble, so I stopped trying to talk. Sometimes she got remote.
But Kathleen wasn't shallow or dumb; she simply didn't
chatter when she didn't feel like it.

There we were that October afternoon, alone in the
Church of the Resurrection—not the Catholic church where
Mr. Pickering got the crane blessed, but an Episcopal one.
It was all right that we were alone in the church; Kathleen
practiced the organ there.

While she fingered *Finlandia* I relaxed and wondered
why Mr. Pickering couldn't have been as lucky in love as
I had been. I will admit, though, that when Kathleen and I

74

started, it wasn't the greatest beginning a love ever had. I was seventeen and a senior; she was sixteen, a junior, and sat three seats ahead of me in French. If it hadn't been for that French class, we'd never have met at all.

"*Un jour, dans le village de Biberich,*" Kathleen had read for the teacher, "*un petit tailleur travaille devant sa fenêtre. Il est le tailleur du village . . .*"

While she recited, I pretended she and I were walking and had the nicest pretend conversation.

"George!"

The teacher's voice brought me back.

"Will you continue reading?"

I stood, hoped I picked the right place, and began:

"*En ce beau moment, le tailleur de Biberich regarde . . .*"

"Kathleen read *that* ten minutes ago," the teacher said. "Of course, if you can't stand the sound of her voice . . ."

The students howled, my face got red, and Kathleen glared.

Three days after that, at the third-floor drinking fountain I wish they'd fix, I met Kathleen and said:

"Listen, how long are you going to hate me? The teacher said that about your voice; I didn't. All right, I'm sorry! What else do I have to do?"

"You could," she said, "turn off the drinking fountain. You're splashing my books."

Four days after *that*, when I passed her locker, she said: "George, I give up. Come here."

I went over.

She looked at me as if I was the sorriest thing ever to come down the pike, sighed, and said:

"You ride the streetcar to Eighth and State, don't you?"

"Yes," I said—and couldn't think of anything to say next. "Well," I said in desperation, "it's a nice streetcar ride. Especially in spring when the windows are open and . . ."

"Here, buster," she grinned, dumping her books into my arms, "*you* can carry these. Come on! We'll miss the car."

That was how we got started but the difference between

us was Sayler Park and Sedamsville. I told you about my neighborhood; Sedamsville with its noise and grime. Well, ride the Sedamsville streetcar west—beyond Sedamsville—and the world changes. The valley, then, is only two streets wide, but the neighborhoods gradually become cleaner. And at the end of the streetcar line was Sayler Park, where Kathleen lived.

When the world began, God made Sayler Park His special window box. There the valley widens. God patted this part and created rises, slopes, and gulleys. He planted trees that were never to die. A few million years later people came along, laid out streets and paths, and built homes no contractor could mass produce, individual, well-mannered, and serene. This was Kathleen's world. It wasn't mine.

At first Kathleen and I were together only on the streetcar. Each evening we rode the Warsaw trolley to Eighth and State, transferred to the Sedamsville car, I rode as far as Sedamsville, and Kathleen rode on alone. When we were lucky, we got cross-seats together. Mostly, though, we dangled from straps. The streetcar ride and the wait at Eighth and State took an hour—the nicest hour in history. We talked about teachers, French verbs, jokes, how I wanted to be a writer, how she wanted to be a musician, how I frowned when I was gloomy, and how she cocked her head when she was stumped. We didn't talk about dances, movies, school plays, or basketball games. That would have meant asking for a date; I was afraid she would say no.

If it hadn't been for the French class we wouldn't have met—and if it hadn't been for a flat tire we wouldn't have kissed. A flat tire on her bike, I mean. I'll never forget that March Saturday as long as I live. I was riding my bike near Anderson Ferry and saw a girl ahead of me, standing by her bike, glaring at it. The girl was Kathleen.

"Pure disaster," she said and pointed at the flat tire. "George, let's hide it in the bushes. When Daddy comes

76

home, he'll come back and get it with the car. Ride me home, okay?"

"But . . ."

"I'm not *that* heavy, am I?"

"Get on," I said.

Heavy? I could have ridden her on my bike for days—uphill. But her hair kept touching my face and it smelled so sweet. I had a hard time keeping my mind on steering.

Before I knew it, I was sitting in her living room, listening to Glenn Miller records, and drinking hot chocolate.

"Penny for your thoughts," she said. Her voice was quiet.

"I don't know," I said. "I was thinking it's nice here. There's something about everything and all."

"I'm glad," she said.

"We're not dating, are we?" I said. "It shouldn't be that way with us."

"I like the way we are," she said.

But I wanted to kiss her.

"Some guys," I said, "just want to kiss girls."

"They make me furious," she said.

"Every guy needs a girl he can talk to," I lied. "Kissing would spoil it."

"I like the way we are," she repeated.

We must have sat ten full minutes without talking. We should have talked, but I had run out of lies, and Kathleen didn't chatter useless chatter. Glenn Miller was "In the Mood," and so was I, but how do you unlock the doors?

Finally I had to say it:

"Are we in love?"

She looked mysterious.

"I don't know," she said.

Also, she looked sad.

"If we are," I said, "let's not kiss too much. I don't want to spoil things."

But it was kiss her then—or never.

She nodded a solemn nod and stood up.

"It'll be all right," I said. But what I said was a question. I didn't know.

Our kiss was kissed.

I felt dizzy.

Kathleen tried a smile, her smile worked, and that was how our love affair began. Call us Puritans, corny and old-fashioned. But that's the way we were. Sex? Kathleen and I talked about that. Love has to be more, if you know what I mean. If that's all love is—Kathleen and I decided—love is the lonesomest game ever invented. It's icing without the taste of cake, or tears without the crying. So much for philosophy. This is Mr. Pickering's story.

Kathleen put the finishing touches on a hymn, readjusted the organ stops, turned the machine off, and smiled at me.

"Still worried about Mr. Pickering?" she said.

She sat beside me in the quiet church and rested her head on my shoulder.

"Well," she said, "he's been nice to you. Be nice to him."

"How?"

"Invite him out to dinner. Invite Mrs. Bruce and surprise him."

"Listen," I said, picturing Mrs. Bruce in a restaurant, "it can't be a fancy place."

I had not given Kathleen the true picture of Mrs. Bruce.

"Don't make it a chili parlor, buster."

"How did you know I was . . ."

"I know you," she said. "Come on. Think of a nice restaurant."

"There's one," I said.

"Which one?"

"It's not the Ritz. No headwaiter or anything."

"George . . ."

"I eat there a lot."

"George . . ."

She kissed me—right in the first pew. With her face inches from mine and her eyes staring daggers at my soul, she said:

78

"Last chance, buster."
I *had* to tell sometime.
"It's Izzy Kadetz's Kosher Restaurant," I said.
"Swell," she sighed.
I don't think she meant it, though.

12

First, Mr. Pickering said no to having dinner with Kathleen and me. "I don't belong in fancy restaurants," he said. I told him it was Izzy Kadetz's. "Oh," he said, perking up, "that's different. I might just think about it."

He thought about it and, in November, said yes.

Second, Mrs. Bruce didn't want to attend. When I telephoned her, she said:

"No need to go out, kid. Come over some night and I'll give you all you want."

"It will be at Izzy Kadetz's," I said—fast.

"That's different," she said. "That's where the vice squad eats."

It was established, after much haggling, that Mrs. Bruce would arrive on her own at Izzy's at seven-thirty. I didn't tell her Mr. Pickering would be there. It was also established that Kathleen and I would meet Mr. Pickering at Eighth and State and arrive at Izzy's by seven-fifteen. I didn't tell him Mrs. Bruce would be there. If all went well, which it didn't, I estimated that before Mrs. Bruce and Mr. Pickering finished their matzoh ball soup, they would be saying love words to each other.

I wasn't surprised they both knew of Izzy Kadetz's Kosher Restaurant. Each day another Cincinnatian "discovers" Izzy's, only to find he was the last to know. Cincinnati has many ordinary restaurants that satisfy the steak-and-potatoes diner. Cincinnati has, also, restaurants that are Italian, German, and Chinese. It has the Spanish Inn, the Greek Coffee House, the Empress Chili Parlor, and the Oyster House. It has more White Castles than you can shake a stick at, on every corner stands a bar & grill, but Cincinnati has only *one* Izzy Kadetz's. Some restaurants employ recorded music to set the mood; Izzy Kadetz's employs the pickle barrel, steam table, and Izzy's shouting. He shouts all the time. His wife does, too. Her name is Rose. I once had the uneasy notion that during their wedding ceremony they shouted so loud that the rabbi, to tie the knot, had to outshout them both. But Izzy and Rose Kadetz are kind and wonderful people. Their shouting is harmless. If you must know, their hearts are as wonderful as their chopped liver.

Kathleen, who didn't know this, was nervous.

"I hope our surprise works," she said as we shivered at Eighth and State, waiting for Mr. Pickering to appear.

"As you say," I said, "it's the least we could do."

"Yes," she said, "but I'm sorry I said it."

"Uh . . . uh . . ."

Mr. Pickering teetered before us. He wore a sport coat that had a torn pocket, a tie that remembered all the soup he'd ever eaten, a white shirt whose collar was tattletale gray and fuzzy, slacks that bagged at the knees and sagged in the seat, his workshoes—greasy and one with no strings—and over his arm he carried his rummage-sale topcoat with the velvet trim on its collar. He wore no hat. November frost chilled his shiny head, but he didn't shiver. When he peered to see if we were the ones he was to meet his breath warmed us and, as they say in gasoline advertising, *winterized* us, too.

"Aren't you cold without a hat?" Kathleen said. "And why don't you put on your coat?"

"Oh," he said, pleased to see that he had brought his coat. "I wondered where she got to."

He struggled into the coat.

"Don't you have a hat?" Kathleen said.

81

"Uh . . . no," he said. "I'm sorry," he added. He hadn't meant to quarrel.

"Let's go, Mr. Pickering," I said. "Here comes a streetcar. It's cold out here."

"I'll tell you what," he said. "You kids go on without me. I'll go buy me a hat."

"No," I said. "You promised to come with us."

"I had a hat once. She was a panama."

"Fine," I said. "Now, come on."

"I don't know what I done with her."

"I've got the car tickets," I said. "Watch your step."

"Oh," he said. "Well, *ladies* first." He stepped aside to let Kathleen climb up into the streetcar, looked to see if any more ladies were on tap, sighed, climbed up into the streetcar, blinked at the motorman, and followed Kathleen back through the car.

"He should be wearing a hat," the motorman told me. "When she's this cold, you oughtn't let your old man run out without no hat."

"He's *not* my father," I said—and hurried through the streetcar to where Kathleen and Mr. Pickering sat.

Kathleen put her fingers to her lips, indicating hush.

"Look," she said.

Mr. Pickering, his cold head bobbing, was sound asleep.

"But just wait," Kathleen murmured. I knew what she meant. Mrs. Bruce's surprise entrance would wake him up fast.

"Remember though," I cautioned Kathleen as the streetcar moved through the West End, "that Mrs. Bruce hasn't been to Sunday school much."

"All right," Kathleen said.

"Don't be upset if sometimes she gets . . . ah . . . earthy," I said.

"I won't," Kathleen said.

"In fact, don't be upset if she's earthy all the time."

"Oh."

"You got to understand, Kathleen. Mrs. Bruce is not like

82

most ladies we know." I thought about this. "She's not like any you've met."

"She'll be nice," said Kathleen, worried.

"Well, yes. I'm glad you said that. She . . . ah . . . likes to *talk*. She has *interests*, you might say. She gets real interested in things. And she's earthy. But don't let her upset you. Underneath it all, she's . . . ah . . . well, she's not much of a lady *there*, either. It would have been nice," I concluded without hope, "if she had been to Sunday school more."

"I don't know what you're trying to tell me," Kathleen said, "but I think you've told me very well."

We fell silent.

Night had come to downtown Cincinnati when I pushed the button that buzzed the buzzer by the motorman's ear to tell him we wanted off at the next stop.

"But in *this* neighborhood?" said Kathleen, staring out the window. "George, there's nothing here but pawnshops and secondhand clothing stores."

"Mr. Pickering," I said, "wake up. Here we are."

"Uh . . . uh . . ." he said, looking around surprised. He wondered what he was doing on a streetcar.

When the trolley stopped at Seventh and Central, the three of us got off. Kathleen, shivering, tucked her arm under mine and looked around apprehensively.

I didn't blame her. Seventh and Central isn't the greatest intersection Cincinnati has. Central Avenue, running north from the Ohio River, divides Cincinnati. On one side is downtown—where, they say, you won't get hit on the head after dark. On the other side is the Negro tenement section called the West End—where, they say, you will get hit on the head after dark, but actually you won't. The West End is mile upon mile of streets lined with two- and three-story tenements that had once been one-family homes of elegance. Now, one family to a room, each building housed dozens of families. Negroes didn't live in the West End because the rent was cheap; they had nowhere else to live. The West End is a rowdy and happy place, but, at the same time, it is a sad and scary district, too. Even the winter chill couldn't erase the smell of decay and some other smells I'll not mention.

"Ain't she nice out, though," Mr. Pickering said, moving along beside us. "You can see the stars. That's how clear she is."

Mr. Pickering hadn't smelled the decay at all.

"*Here?*" Kathleen repeated, her voice low. "This is the neighborhood where . . ."

"Not *here*," I said. "*There!*" I pointed across the street to Izzy Kadetz's Kosher Restaurant.

The restaurant occupied a two-story brick building that had seen better days. On either side—buttoned up for the night, their windows barred and iron grating blocking their doorways—stood a brace of pawnshops. Their windows, each lighted by one naked bulb, showed a shadowy display of shotguns, mandolins, wristwatches, false teeth, power tools, clothing, and knives—all secondhand. The storefront windows of Izzy's, however, were brightly lit, drenched with steam, and cheery. Piled about, with no attempt at order, was a disorder of beer and wine bottles, boxes of matzos in the window so long the sun had faded the lettering, bottles of champagne marked with a dusty sign that said VINTAGE! CHEAP!, and another sign, more ornate but just as vintage, that said CUSTOMER WANTED!

"It looks . . . nice," said Kathleen as I ushered them in.

Izzy's *was* nice. Well-lighted, full of cooking aromas, and warm, his restaurant made the dread of the night vanish. Izzy's—with its ancient pickle barrel, its litter, and its full-bodied smells—was sanctuary.

We stopped just inside the front door. Stacked around, as if they'd just arrived, were cases of beer, piles of matzoh boxes, and—of course—that pickle barrel. Its heady flavor almost knocked you down. In front, also, was Izzy's office: the glass-front and glass-topped counter stuffed with cigar boxes, cigarette cartons, boxes of halvahs, and receipts for the last two dozen years. On top of the glass counter stood

84

the cash register and the toothpick machine. Izzy, who possessed no talent as a window trimmer, had no talent at interior design, either. Lining one wall in the front were shelves filled with bottles of wine, each bottle marked VINTAGE! CHEAP! In Izzy's heart, every year was a vintage year.

At that hour of the evening, his restaurant was empty. Izzy's big business was at noon.

Izzy Kadetz—a huge and worried-looking man who wore a white apron that came to his shoe tops—moved forward to greet us.

"Sit anywhere!" he shouted. He steered us to the tables in the rear. "What do you think you need: reservations!"

Kathleen relaxed her tight hold. She felt safe again. Izzy's loud voice—somehow—is magic that creates tranquillity.

Tables that seated eight jutted out from the right wall in the rear of the restaurant. On the opposite wall was the heart and soul of Izzy's restaurant: the steam table. Customers could sit wherever they pleased—or, at noon, wherever there was a chair open. One day at lunch I shared the table with two policemen, a lawyer, a rabbi with a beard, a doctor, a radio announcer, and a Negro junkman; but they kept arriving, eating, and departing. When I finished I was sitting with a city councilman, two garage mechanics, an advertising copywriter, a bus driver, a detective, and handcuffed to the detective an angry man who glared at the rest of us.

Kadetz's Kosher Restaurant at 637 Central Avenue had located well. The city hall—that dull, granite blob that filled a city block—was a few steps north and its tenants ate at Izzy's. A few steps the other direction, facing one another, stood the Plum Street temple, with its two minarets that sprouted fifty feet above its roof line, and the Old Cathedral of St. Peter in Chains, fashioned after a Greek temple with massive Corinthian columns that supported its massive portico. A synagogue and a Roman Catholic church, as neighbors, made good sense. Their customers were, also, Izzy's customers—and at Izzy's didn't they sit together and eat as neighbors? Man has a body and a soul; and that neighborhood—thanks to the city hall, synagogue, church, and Izzy Kadetz's—could service any need that came along.

"Well, what'll it be!" Izzy shouted when we were seated. "I got some nice roast beef!" He stopped and stared at Mr. Pickering. "You should wear a hat!" he shouted. "You'll freeze your skin!"

"Uh . . . uh . . ." said Mr. Pickering, shattered.

"Tell the gentleman I'm kidding!" Izzy shouted at the world. "Tell him I should be Jack Benny I'm so funny!"

Izzy's warmth warmed Mr. Pickering.

"That's okay," said Mr. Pickering. "I should have a hat. I had a panama once. I don't know what I did with her."

"I know a guy that can get you one wholesale!" Izzy offered.

"Uh . . . maybe later."

"Right now, have some chopped liver!" Izzy shouted. "I made it special! It's imported! It's . . ."

"Could I have a beer first?" said Mr. Pickering.

"Be a sport! Order champagne!"

"No," said Mr. Pickering. "I'd just like . . ."

"Then order wine! We got a special this week!"

"A beer would be . . ."

"The last of the big-time spenders!" Izzy shouted. "Okay! I'll get you a beer!" Izzy looked at me. "Some champagne for your shikse?"

"Shikse?" I said.

"She's one of you! Izzy said. "She's not one of us!"

"Shikse?"

"A *gentile* girl! Where you been?"

"I'm a shikse?" Kathleen grinned. She was getting the biggest kick out of Izzy.

"If you want religious instruction, go down one block!" Izzy shouted. "Here you eat!"

"What's good?" Kathleen said.

Izzy looked hurt.

86

"Everything!" he shouted. "But some," he added, "is better than some other! What would you like! No! Don't tell me!" He padded back to the steam table. "I'll fix the lady a feast!" he shouted. "She gives this place some class! So tell your friends!"

He was a blur of action.

Kathleen touched my arm.

"Hadn't we better wait?" she said. She looked at me with meaning. "You know . . ."

"That's right," I said. It wouldn't do to order before Mrs. Bruce arrived.

I walked to the steam table, where Izzy was beside himself *creating*. Window display was not his strong point. Neither was interior design. But surround him with roast beef, salami, corned beef, pastrami, vegetable soup, pickles, cabbage, pumpernickel buns, onion rolls, rye bread, potato pancakes, and steam—and he is pure genius. As I said, the heart and soul of Izzy Kadetz's Kosher Restaurant is its steam table. It is to Izzy what paints were to Rembrandt. Izzy's brushes are his spoons, ladles, and knives. His colors are ten thousand flavors: soups, meats, gravies, baked goods, and pickles. His canvas is each plate he serves— and each plate is a masterpiece. Izzy is the loud and angry master of the sandwich; he is heavy-handed with the sandwich's contents: not slices of meat, but *mounds* of meat. The breads he cuts himself. No namby-pamby machine-sliced pieces: each slice is a huge and beautiful slab. At Izzy's a sandwich is a full meal and a full meal is murder.

"Well!" he shouted, looking up from the plate he was creating. "What do you want?"

"We're not ready to eat yet," I said. "We'd like to . . ."

"What do you think I'm running: a streetcar stop?"

"We'd like some wine first," I said fast.

He relented.

"For you," he said, "a special price!"

"We'd like . . ."

"Don't tell me!" he shouted, setting aside Kathleen's plate and wiping his hands. "For you, the best!"

I had visions of bankruptcy. Izzy was wise. He saw the vision I had.

He grabbed my arm and hustled me out of earshot of the others to the front of the store.

"Kid," he said. He surprised me by talking low. "I like you. It's on the house."

"But . . ."

"Don't tell me how to run my business!" he shouted, himself again. He pulled a bottle from the shelf, blew the dust off it, and shouted, "What are you doing up here! Back to the table! You think I got nothing to do but stand around and talk!"

That is Izzy Kadetz: loud, brash, angry, and quarrelsome —but underneath, he's a softie.

He set the wine on the table, brought glasses (including one for himself), sat beside Kathleen, opened the wine, and poured.

"You got a nice guy here!" Izzy shouted at Kathleen. "Too bad he's a goy! He might have made something of himself!"

Kathleen smiled.

"I think he's nice, too," she said.

She raised her glass of wine.

"To Izzy Kadetz's Kosher Restaurant," she said. "And to George, who's only a goy; and to Mr. Pickering, the best machinist the New York Central ever had; and to . . ."

"What about me, you floozy!"

We turned, our glasses suspended in the air.

Mrs. Bruce was standing beside the pickle barrel, glaring at us.

"Mrs. Bruce," I said, wishing I were anywhere else, "I'd like you to meet Kathleen. Kathleen, may I . . ."

Mrs. Bruce wasn't listening. She had reached into the pickle barrel and grabbed herself a big one. She stood by the barrel, gobbling the pickle down. She reached in and

88

fished out another, ate it, wiped the wet from her hands on the front of her dress and said:

"I don't know about the rest of you, but pickles make me horny."

On that note, the dinner party began.

13

Izzy watched Mrs. Bruce reach, up to her elbows, into the pickle barrel and he was impressed. He looked upon her as a container to be filled. She was the biggest container he had ever seen. On the other hand, he had seen containers that were neater.

Kathleen was becalmed. She sat, wineglass hoisted in the air, her mouth open, and had no expression on her face. I thought she was in a coma, but she wasn't. She blinked once.

Mr. Pickering, surprised and pleased, was the only one who moved.

"Uh . . . uh . . ." he said and started to get up.

"Beershot!" Mrs. Bruce bellowed, seeing him for the first time. Her eyes narrowed with hate. She stopped sloshing around the pickle barrel, straightened up, and sneered, "Well, well, well! Look what the cat drug in!"

It took her several minutes to say it because, as you know, she embellished a lot.

"Mrs. Bruce," I said, trying to get the dinner party organized, "we've saved a place for you."

She padded through the restaurant toward us.

"But not next to *that* freak," she said, frowning at Mr. Pickering. "Them pickles has got more manhood than . . ."

"Uh . . . uh . . . Rosalind . . ."

She refused to look at him. She glared at me.

90

"Well, you invited me here to eat. Let's get on with it."
Izzy sprang to life.

"What'll it be!" he shouted. "We got . . ."

"*FOOD!*" she bellowed. "That's why I came. I didn't come to see him!" She shattered Mr. Pickering with a stare. "I came to *eat!*"

"Uh . . . uh . . . Rosalind . . ."

"*FOOD!*"

"Lady," shouted Izzy, desperate, "what'll you have!"

"*EVERYTHING!*"

I touched Kathleen's arm.

"Why don't you put down your wine if you're not going to drink it," I said. "It might spill."

Dreamlike, Kathleen put the glass on the table.

From behind the steam table, Izzy shouted:

"First, chopped liver!"

"Swell," Mrs. Bruce grimaced. "Gimme a pound on an onion roll."

"Fat lady, did you say a *pound?*" Izzy shouted.

"*FOOD!*"

"A pound of chopped liver on an onion roll, coming up!"

"Uh . . . uh . . . Rosalind . . ."

"I got nothing to say to you, Beershot! And what it is, is: you and me is through!"

"But, Rosalind . . ."

"*I came here to eat!*"

"But, Rosalind . . ."

"*FOOD!*"

Izzy, the master, worked fast. He filled the table with chopped-liver sandwiches, pastrami sandwiches, corned-beef sandwiches, matzoh-ball soup, vegetable soup, dishes of baked potatoes, mounds of potato pancakes, bowls of sour cabbage, and bottles of cream soda. Mrs. Bruce waded in. She attacked his provisions with gusto. Kathleen, Izzy, and I watched in amazement, but Mr. Pickering watched with pride. She bolted sandwiches, ate sliced pickles by the fistful, drank bottles of cream soda in two gulps, and during intermission—when Izzy hurried to replenish her fodder—she grazed off potato pancakes, sour cabbage, and halvah candy bars. She wasted no time on conversation. She had not come to be sociable. She had come to eat.

"Look at that fat lady go!" Izzy shouted as he sliced another pound of pastrami. "Two customers like her, I retire to Florida, and live on Easy Street!"

"*Gumble, gumble!*" she mumbled, her mouth a traffic jam of hot pastrami. Her greasy fingers indicated her plate was empty and that she wanted more.

"Here!" shouted Izzy, running to the table with reinforcements. "Eat in good health, fat lady!"

"*Gumble, gumble!*" she sneered, wiped her hands on the front of her dress, and began again.

"You bring me nice customers, kid!" Izzy shouted. "Her I will feed wholesale."

I think Kathleen was more disturbed by Mrs. Bruce's eating habits than I was. Kathleen had never eaten in the roundhouse—during the first trick, I mean. At night we ate when we felt like it and slept during the twenty-minute lunch hour, but the twenty-minute lunch on the first trick was a twenty-minute spectacular of shouts, plates rattling, and steam—all concentrated in the locker room.

The man who ran one of the railroad restaurants (sleeping rooms upstairs) in Sedamsville came each day to the roundhouse to set up a steam table and dish out hot lunches. His lunches, they say, were good. His roast beef swam in gravy, his pies were great wedges of beauty, and his coffee was strong, piping hot, and blacker than the blacksmith's fingernails. The lunch hour, though, lasted only twenty minutes.

He had no time to think of money. Surrounded by steam, overcome by the din, all he saw was a panic of hands. They reached through the steam, grabbed his plate lunches and his sandwiches, and vanished. The excitement was so intense, the steam so thick, and the interval so short, the restaurant man was never certain *who* ate *what*. When the lunch hour was done, the men swarmed from the locker room, shouting:

"Plate lunch! Coffee!"

"Ham on white! Pepsi!"

"Peach pie! Milk!"

"Pepsi! Cake!"

"Coffee! Lunch!"

It was his task to attach a name to each voice and write down the cost of what the voice's owner ate. Whether or not he charged the right amount, he never discovered. Twice a month, after payday, the roundhouse crew hurled money at him and shouted:

"I owe you this!"

"Here you are!"

"This covers me!"

"You owe me fifteen cents! Work it out!"

In addition to settling accounts, they also shouted:

"Plate lunch! Coffee!"

"Ham on white! Pepsi!"

"Peach pie! Milk!"

"Pepsi! Cake!"

"Coffee! Lunch!"

Whether or not the restaurant man made money, only he knew. But lunch was exciting. Maybe he showed up for that.

What I'm saying is, railroad men—with only twenty minutes for lunch—are not slow eaters. I don't know what Mrs. Bruce's excuse was.

All I know is, with a belch that torpedoed the evening, unnerved Kathleen, unhinged me, rattled the bottles on the shelves, frightened Izzy, but impressed Mr. Pickering, Mrs. Bruce pushed her chair from the table, did it again, and said:

"Well, kiddies, I hate to eat and run . . ."

". . . Wait!" I said.

She had been in the restaurant only fifteen minutes, our table was a disaster area, Kathleen's eyes were glazed, but to me, it was then or never.

93

She had been invited for a *reason*, and the reason was sitting across the table from her, looking at her with love.

"Her trouble," Mr. Pickering had said once, "is that nobody loves her like I do."

"Maybe they're right and you're wrong," I had said.

"Maybe," he had said, "but there you are. She's a bitter pill to swallow, kid, but there's something about her that makes me come all over queer. She's a special kind of bird. Maybe it's all that fat. There ain't none like her anywhere else. Just before God made her, He broke the mold."

"What you mean is . . ."

". . . Kid, I know what I mean. I mean, there she is, beautiful. I love her. Don't somebody have to? Can't it be me? I mean, there is no love like the love you love a fat bird with."

Philosophy like that had been hard to dispute, but there she sat, ready to waddle out the door and break Mr. Pickering's heart all over again. I couldn't let that happen.

"Kid," said Mrs. Bruce, annoyed, "I came to eat. Well, I ate. Now, I'm going!" Her eyes narrowed. "Course, if you got some other need? If this floozy—" she poked a fat thumb at Kathleen "—don't know how yet, I . . ."

"Have another cream soda!" Izzy shouted, his face red. "Cream soda for everybody!" he shouted and hustled to get it.

"Rosalind," said Mr. Pickering, "that nice little girl is a nice little girl. You shouldn't . . ."

"*That* does it!" Mrs. Bruce bellowed. She slammed her fist on the table and upset the bottles of cream soda Izzy had just put there. She was a hornet's nest of hate.

"You insult me in front of this floozy who ain't . . ."

"*Mrs. Bruce!*"

Kathleen was standing. Her face was white. She was trembling with anger I didn't know she possessed. And there were tears in her eyes.

"Darn you," she said, half crying, "must you drag everybody down to your level! Darn you, Mrs. Bruce, what are you trying to do to us!"

"Kathleen, wait . . ." I said, touching her arm.

She jerked away from my touch.

"You can say what you want about me," Kathleen said. I had never seen her that distraught. "Because I don't know you and you don't know me, we'll never see each other again, and it will all be lies anyway. But, Mrs. Bruce, you're more awful than I dreamed. You're the most awful person I've ever met. But don't you see what you're doing? You're hurting Mr. Pickering! Can't you see that? *You're hurting Mr. Pickering!*"

"*He's a nobody!*" Mrs. Bruce screeched. She made other comments we'll not list here.

Kathleen, amazed by Mrs. Bruce's venom, was speechless.

But when Mrs. Bruce began to rattle off particulars, Kathleen found her voice again and stopped Mrs. Bruce cold with:

"No! Mr. Pickering is not those things. He's the best machinist the New York Central has."

Mrs. Bruce was becalmed. "What has *that*," she seemed to be thinking, "have to do with what *I'm* talking about?"

Mr. Pickering was pleased that Kathleen had come to his rescue, but he was puzzled, too. What she had said about him had sounded nice, but what had she said?

Izzy jumped into the breach.

"More cream soda!" he shouted.

And he hustled away to get it.

But Kathleen was running out of steam. Anger would never be her greatest weapon.

"All we wanted," Kathleen said, "was for you and Mr. Pickering to . . . to . . . get together again. That's all we wanted, Mrs. Bruce."

Kathleen, forlorn, sank back into her chair.

She was ashamed. That she had been angry and screamed shocked her.

When she spoke, she spoke low, but she spoke the words that in her world she had to say.

"I'm sorry, Mrs. Bruce. I shouldn't have shouted. I had no right. I apologize . . ."

Mrs. Bruce sneered.

They were from different planets; they didn't understand each other. Mrs. Bruce took Kathleen's apology for weakness and surrender. She didn't know that inside Kathleen was not soft; inside Kathleen was steel. She didn't know that Kathleen's planet had demanded that Kathleen apologize. She had never seen the beauty inside Kathleen's heart; she wouldn't have understood it if she had seen it. All Mrs. Bruce saw was a floozy who turned tail. Mrs. Bruce swelled with victory; she thought she had won; she didn't know Kathleen at all.

But Kathleen didn't understand Mrs. Bruce, either. Kathleen had been shocked by the older woman's language, dismayed by the force of the older woman's fury, and repelled by the sight of her slovenliness. But Kathleen had stepped in where she was not supposed to enter: an older woman's life. Kathleen would have made no such attempt to interfere in the lives of her mother and daddy, nor in the lives of any of her parents' friends. They were the elders. They deserved respect. That was why, even though she thought she was right, she knew she was wrong—and apologized.

They looked at each other in silence; each got out of the silence what they thought was there. They didn't know that each was playing a different game with different rules; they thought they were playing a game together.

"Uh . . . uh . . ." said Mr. Pickering, who had learned something else. The realization had come slowly, but it got there and awed him. The event had been no accident. The event had been *planned* so he could see Mrs. Bruce again!

It didn't matter, to him, that things had not gone as scheduled. What mattered to him was we had tried to help him. This thought dazzled Mr. Pickering.

"Uh . . . uh . . ." he said. He couldn't find words to say.

When he did find words, he said them with hesitation. His voice was shy.

96

"Ain't you birds sweet," he said. "You birds is so sweet. Ain't these birds sweet, Rosalind? Don't you see? They *planned* this thing. It was a surprise. They planned . . ."

He stopped, shook his head in disbelief, looked at Izzy, and said:

"These sweet birds *planned* this whole thing. They . . ."

But he couldn't go on. The idea was too stunning. He brought out his handkerchief and blew his nose with a great honking noise that said, "I love everybody in the world!"

Mrs. Bruce, unable to translate honks, stood up. She was filled with chopped liver and loathing.

"I can tell when I ain't wanted," she brayed.

"Uh . . . uh . . ."

"Me and you, Beershot, *was* through, *is* through, and that's that!" she bellowed. She bellowed some other stuff, too. She concluded with, "You can't swing on my garden gate no more!"

"Aw, Rosalind, don't be that way in front of these sweet little kids. They . . ."

Mrs. Bruce stiffened.

". . . is only trying," Mr. Pickering went on, "to help you and me. That sweet little thing ain't like you. And the kid, there, ain't like me. But they're good birds. I'm a nobody, and you got your mouth."

"Mr. Pickering . . ." I said.

He shook his head.

"No," he said. "This is why you got to get out of the roundhouse, kid." He looked at Kathleen. His eyes were troubled. "Don't *you* see why? There's nothing there but me and talk of fat women."

Mrs. Bruce boiled—but Mr. Pickering, in his love for us, had forgotten his other love.

Mrs. Bruce whirled—a bedraggled, messy whirl—and stomped to the door, shook more bottles en route; the door *slammed*, Mrs. Bruce was gone, and the party was over.

The three of us at the table didn't speak. There was no happiness anywhere.

97

From behind the steam table, Izzy shouted:
"I got it figured out!"

He waved brown wrapping paper at us. Numbers were scrawled on it.

"Adding the pounds of this and the pounds of that," he shouted, "she went out eleven pounds heavier than she came in! That's an estimate! Who knows what a pickle weighs!"

He came to our table, sat with us, and sipped tea from a glass. He looked from Kathleen, to me, to Mr. Pickering, and wanted to cheer us.

"What is this!" he shouted. "What goes on! Be happy! Look at the bright side! You got to see that fat lady eat! You should be telephoning Ripley!"

But we sat in silence.

With a sigh, Izzy went to the beer case, opened a bottle of beer, returned, placed it in front of Mr. Pickering; and when Izzy spoke, his voice was gentle.

"I can get you a deal on a hat," he said.

"Thank you," said Mr. Pickering.

Mr. Pickering's voice, though, was sad and far away.

"Mr. Pickering?"

He looked at Kathleen.

"Go after her," she said.

Mr. Pickering didn't answer.

"She needs you," Kathleen said.

Mr. Pickering didn't move.

"Kathleen is right," I said. "Go after her."

He shook his head.

"What we had," he said, "we never had. And what we never had is over."

He drank his beer.

He never seemed lonelier.

Kathleen touched his hand.

"Mr. Pickering," she said, "I love you."

She sounded like she was going to cry.

But he didn't look at her.

And that was that.

14

"Therapy!" beamed Mr. Duveneck.

"Therapy?" I said.

"Beershot needs therapy," said Mr. Duveneck.

He shadowboxed his way off the turntable.

"Come on," he said.

"Therapy?"

"It's in a pamphlet I read," said Mr. Duveneck and dodged. The World's Heavyweight Champion had almost socked him. "Beershot has been mooning around since you and him went to Izzy Kadetz's. Kid, he drags like he's never dragged before. He needs therapy."

"Therapy?"

We walked through the roundhouse to the locker room.

"To get his *mind* off things," Mr. Duveneck said. He pretended to skip rope. "To build his muscles. Therapy will do wonders for his astragalus."

"Astragalus?"

Mr. Duveneck drank hot celery juice from his thermos.

"Kid," he said, "I'm going to level with you. I happen to *like* Beershot."

"But what has that . . ."

"I'll admit he drinks. He's usually drunker than seven hundred dollars. But now, *whew!* He is buzzed; he's bombed. He isn't sampling the sauce; he's wading in it. He isn't . . ."

"I *get* the idea," I said. "But what has . . ."

"He's sadder than he used to be. Have you noticed?"

"Yes, but . . ."

"And he *leans* more. That bothers me. He stands around, leans, and *stares*."

"But . . ."

"Last night he started to lean and there was nothing there. Kid, if I hadn't grabbed him, he'd have fallen into the drop pit and hurt something."

"Swell, Mr. Duveneck, but . . ."

"I'll bet he's somewhere now: leaning and staring. What he needs is therapy."

We were back where we began, so I said:

"Therapy?"

"Yeah. Therapy. I got this pamphlet . . ."

And Mr. Duveneck, back where he began, began again. His idea was muscle tone. He felt Mr. Pickering was moping because his muscles didn't have any. I didn't tell Mr. Duveneck the *real* reason. It wouldn't have mattered. Mr. Duveneck, that night, was peddling therapy.

Well, Mr. Pickering *was* dragging. No question about it. He had been bad before, but after that dinner party, he was worse. When Mrs. Bruce had left Izzy Kadetz's, Mr. Pickering just sat and drank beer. And wine. And cream soda. He drank a lot, but he didn't say a word. It had gotten late, Kathleen and I didn't want to leave him, but Izzy with great understanding had waved us out and opened another beer for Mr. Pickering. Anyway, there was nothing any of us could do. When Mrs. Bruce walked out, Mr. Pickering's reason for living had walked out with her. But the next night he was at the roundhouse and, as Mr. Duveneck said, "drunker than seven hundred dollars." Something had to be done. I couldn't bear to see him that way week after week. So I listened to Mr. Duveneck because maybe the hostler was right. Maybe Mr. Pickering's astragalus needed an overhaul. Anything was worth a try.

I followed Mr. Duveneck to the deadhouse where—leaning and staring—Mr. Pickering stood.

100

He didn't even say hello when we stood in front of his stare.

Mr. Duveneck thought a minute, then shouted: *"RUG WEAVING!"*

That got Mr. Pickering. He shuddered.

It got me, too.

"Rug weaving?" I said.

"BEERSHOT! IT'S THERAPY!" Mr. Duveneck shouted. He had Mr. Pickering's attention. He didn't want to lose it.

"Uh . . . uh . . ." said Mr. Pickering. His voice was pale and thin, but those were the first words he had said in three days. I almost cheered.

"IT'S WHAT YOU NEED!" Mr. Duveneck shouted. *"YOU GOT TO STOP LEANING AND STARING! RUG WEAVING!"*

"Rug weaving?" Mr. Pickering mumbled and breathed on us. I was glad no lighted torches were near. The round-house would have exploded.

I won't recite the entire conversation. It lasted two noisy hours. There was a lot of shouting about Mr. Pickering's astragalus. There was a lot of shouting about rug weaving. There was shouting because now and then, even with shouting, Mr. Pickering seemed to fade away. When he did, Mr. Duveneck started over again. Finally, Mr. Pickering blurred, did agree that he was doing himself no good, wasn't a credit to the New York Central railroad, muttered that maybe therapy was the answer, got teary because we loved him, but hesitated at rug weaving because, as he pointed out, he had no loom. Mr. Duveneck shouted there were other kinds of therapy. The hostler suggested basket-weaving, which Mr. Pickering vetoed. Embroidering was suggested, which Mr. Pickering vetoed. The hostler suggested flower-arranging; on that suggestion Mr. Pickering faded again, and Mr. Duveneck had to start from the beginning. He didn't suggest flower-arranging the next time around.

"BUT YOU GOT TO KEEP BUSY," the hostler shouted.

"GET YOUR MIND OFF THINGS, STOP LEANING, AND GIVE UP STARING, OR YOUR CORACOBRACHIALIS WILL RUST. THEN WHERE'D YOU BE!"

"I'm not sure," Mr. Pickering mumbled, impressed. Mr. Duveneck had gotten through to him.

"IF YOU DON'T WANT TO WEAVE RUGS . . ."

"I'd rather not," said Mr. Pickering. "And don't shout. I can hear you."

"OH!"

Mr. Duveneck felt therapy was at work already.

"Then, at least," the hostler said, "do railroad things. *RAILROAD THINGS, BEERSHOT!*"

"I do railroad things every day," said Mr. Pickering, sorry he had to argue, but there it was.

"Well," said Mr. Duveneck, "help *others* do *their* railroad things."

Mr. Pickering looked around: all he saw was us and the vast emptiness of the deadhouse.

"What others?" he said.

"Well . . . uh . . . go help the callboy!"

"Sourpuss Landsdowne?"

"Yeah. Sourpuss Landsdowne."

"Help *him?*"

"Help him do railroad things. *His* railroad things."

"But Sourpuss Landsdowne?"

"Beershot, it will get your mind off things."

"Still, Sourpuss Landsdowne . . ."

". . . IT'S THERAPY!"

Mr. Pickering winced.

"Well," he said, "she's worth a try."

"Go ahead!" said Mr. Duveneck. "It's just what the doctor ordered."

We watched Mr. Pickering float out through the deadhouse door. Just before he disappeared, Mr. Duveneck shouted:

"AND DON'T LEAN SO MUCH!"

Mr. Pickering, tilted, was gone. We didn't realize the Pandora's box Mr. Duveneck had opened. What we saw was a friend coming out of his shell.

"I hope Mr. Landsdowne understands," I said.

Mr. Duveneck began shadowboxing.

"Callboys don't know enough even to eat Wheaties!" he said—the worst thing he could say about anyone.

Mr. Landsdowne, the callboy, was forty-one years old. His nickname, as you may have guessed, was Sourpuss. He had been a callboy since February 4, 1915. On that day, he had lied about his age, the railroad had hired him, and (Mr. Pickering said) the Germans blockaded Great Britain. Mr. Landsdowne never married. "What woman would marry a callboy," the callboy said once. "I ain't even got a job that has a man's title. I can't get married being a callboy, can I, but don't worry about me. I get my ashes hauled regular." What made him sour, and he seemed to sour more each year, was waiting for the seniority system to promote him to a higher job. Six men had to die first, or retire; and they expressed little interest in either. He had been waiting twenty-six years for promotion and his patience, at times, wore thin. But he said, "I eat three squares a day. That's more'n your old man did during the depression." He wasn't a pleasant fellow at all.

He was tall, bony, frail, and vain. He had the pallor men get who never see the sun. His hair, which he combed fifty million times a night, was wavy, gray, and greasy. His nose was too big, his eyes were too small, his chin was too long, his forehead was short, his weight was too little, and his vanity was too much. He said he didn't marry because he was a callboy; I think he didn't marry because no lady would have him. I doubt if he even got his ashes hauled. No one liked him. He smelled of after-shave lotion, talcum powder, Juicy-Fruit gum, and—during winter—of Vicks. He thought he owned the railroad.

I must be honest with you. I've *never* liked Mr. Landsdowne. When I was a boy and my father and I would be winding the cat whiskers on a crystal set, playing the Victrola, or driving nails, Mr. Landsdowne would pound on our front door and shout, *"You're called! You're called!"* My father would go to the door, find what run he was called for, and my mother would pack his lunch box. My father would climb into his overalls, tie a red railroad handkerchief around his neck; wink at me, and be gone. Sometimes he would not come home until the next day because of a mix-up in deadheading. That's why, when I was young, I didn't like Mr. Landsdowne. He took my father away. But when I came to work in the roundhouse and got to know Mr. Landsdowne better, I realized I hated him.

Callboys are needed, though. Railroads don't run, as grocery stores do, at regular hours. Even the runs that are scheduled—passenger runs, freight, transfers, locals, and the rest—can confuse you. Suppose you're firing the Valley Local. No matter what the timetable says, it doesn't leave the yards the same time each day. You go when the run is "called" and the run isn't called until the locomotive is ready and the freight cars are assembled. Sometimes the trouble is with the transfers that take freight cars to the L&N in exchange for others. If the transfers are late, the yard crew that makes up your train is late, and so the Valley Local starts late. It's the engine dispatcher's job to call crews when everything is ready and not before. Otherwise he has a nasty problem with overtime. Well, the engine dispatcher gives the crew names to the callboy and on the third trick the callboy, Mr. Landsdowne, who thinks he's president of the railroad, calls the crew.

Most of the time Mr. Landsdowne used the telephone. He shouted into it, *"You're called! You're called!"*—followed with details of what, where, and sometimes why. Wrong numbers provoked him. It didn't matter that he'd roused a streetcar motorman at 3 A.M.; Mr. Landsdowne shouted, *"You're called! You're called!"* at whoever mumbled hello. Only after the callboy had shouted the details could the person called get a word in edgewise and some of the words were not always polite. Once I was in the engine dispatcher's office when this happened. Mr. Landsdowne listened in anger to an old lady trying to convince him she wouldn't fire the Guilford Hill pusher because she didn't work for the railroad, and finally, full of fury, he cursed her and shouted, "If I called the wrong number, why did you answer the phone!" No, he was not a pleasant fellow.

When not sitting in the engine dispatcher's office and sneering at the rest of us because we were dirty and he wasn't, Mr. Landsdowne would be hurrying through the Sedamsville night in search of crews to alert. When the engineer or fireman who didn't have a telephone lived within two miles of the roundhouse, the callboy had to track him down. He pounded on doors of flat buildings, hurled rocks at what he assumed were the right bedroom windows, and bellowed to whoever answered, *"You're called! You're called!"* Or, if he sought crewmen laying over in Cincinnati, he stumbled along pitch-black halls in railroad rooming houses and beat a tattoo on any door that struck his fancy, regardless of the room's contents. If the wrong man answered, Mr. Landsdowne charged it off to bum luck and, until he found the fireman or engineer he required, pounded on the rest of the doors. Usually, by the time he left the railroad rooming house, he had awakened all its occupants, including those who were not railroad men but were fallen women who now and then visited the transient railroaders to haul their ashes. So said Mr. Landsdowne, the authority. His job was thankless, he earned the title Sourpuss every waking minute of his day, but callboys were important to railroads. Without them, no crews would appear and trains would stop running.

I didn't see the scene between Mr. Pickering and Mr. Landsdowne, but I did see the results of it: an engine dispatcher's nightmare.

Apparently, when Mr. Pickering went to see the callboy, the callboy was in a bad mood. The engine dispatcher had assigned him too many crews to call in too short a time, and most of them were unreachable by telephone, so he welcomed Mr. Pickering's offer to help. I don't think he welcomed it gracefully and with good cheer (he was graceless and had no good cheer), but the point is, he said Mr. Pickering could help him do his railroad things.

"I need an assistant anyway," he later told the board of inquiry. "Actually, I need three assistants. I need a department. You don't realize the work I have."

He was the first empire builder I had ever met. Since, in business, I've met lots of them.

But this is not a manual that tells you how to be a corporate success. This is about Mr. Pickering.

Well, Mr. Landsdowne asked Mr. Pickering to telephone the crew for the Guilford Hill pusher. The pusher was scheduled to double-head with a freight running extra at 7 A.M. until they reached Sunman, Indiana; there cut away, coast back down Guilford Hill, and push other trains up the grade, too.

"I told him to call the engineer and fireman," Mr. Landsdowne told the board of inquiry. "I could have done it myself but I had to chase the crew for the extra freight, not to mention three other crews for three other runs. They were sleeping in one of five rooming houses and nobody knew which was where. But all Beershot had to do was telephone. Was that asking too much?"

The way things turned out, it was asking a lot.

"All I know is," Mr. Pickering said later, saddened by the adventure, "Sourpuss Landsdowne was gone like a bird. Maybe he said which engineer he wanted me to call and which fireman. It doesn't really matter. The important thing is, the Guilford Hill pusher needed a crew, I'm not good at remembering names; history is where I shine, and I had to call somebody, didn't I?"

He ended up calling everybody.

No one realized the immensity of his effort until six-thirty that morning when engine crews began to stack up in the engine dispatcher's office. By this time Mr. Pickering, sleepy, was dozing somewhere in a firebox and Mr. Landsdowne had yet to return from his rounds of the railroad boarding-houses.

The engine dispatcher sensed something was wrong when John Harpham, who was supposed to be at the Cincinnati Union Terminal to fire his assigned passenger run to Indianapolis, showed up at Riverside instead. When three firemen from the extra board—Gene Williamson, Alan Schulz, and Leo Hirtl—also appeared, the engine dispatcher began to feel jumpy. By six thirty-five, four other firemen had arrived (three were not supposed to be there because they had assigned yard jobs and the fourth was supposed to be on vacation), as well as engineers Gregory Schlier, John Fink, Bob Cromie, Dan Wickenden, and Glenn Schnitker. They stood in angry groups and did not try to hide their irritation: they had *all* showed up to work the Guilford Hill pusher: eight firemen, five engineers, and—looking bewildered but willing to give it a try—the second-trick yard clerk, Leo Underhill.

"No," moaned the engine dispatcher.

"Yes," said the men. "We was called and here we is."

They began, with a vengeance, to fill out time cards.

"But," said the engine dispatcher, trying to make sense out of the fiasco, "why are *you* here, Harpham? You're supposed to be at the C.U.T. right now. You're firing passenger. You're . . ."

"I figured I was bumped," said Harpham, irritated. "Anyway, I wasn't called there. I was called here."

"I don't know too much about shoveling coal," said the yard clerk. "But you know me: I'll try anything once."

"How many pushers you *got*?" said Glenn Schnitker, the engineer. He was testy. "That hill is going to get awful crowded," he added, looking at the others and counting noses. "And my regular job is the east yard, you know."

"Then why are you . . ."

"Because I was called!" he said, and that was that.

"You called me in before my time," offered another fireman. "I'll be doglawed before I reach Valley Junction."

By then, when I walked into the engine dispatcher's of-

fice, the room looked like a convention no one wanted to
attend. The two telephones on the dispatcher's desk were
ringing, but the engine dispatcher—his face white—sat
stunned. He didn't believe it. He thought he was having a
bad dream. He was waiting to wake up.

Mr. Landsdowne hustled in, frowned at the crews with
distaste, and combed his hair.

"I been looking all over for half you guys," he complained.
He rattled off crew assignments to most. When the ones with
regular runs began muttering angry things about a nation-
wide railroad strike, the engine dispatcher snapped from his
lethargy and placated the disrupted men by calling each a
taxicab at railroad expense and sending them to where they
should have been sent in the first place.

The fireman who had been called in from vacation, however, refused to be cajoled. He was young and full of anger.
He stomped out and didn't say a word, and the New York
Central never saw him again. When last seen, he was firing
on the B&O and had a dazed look about him.

The yard clerk, tremendously relieved, went home and
put a damp cloth on his forehead.

"I hate to think what this cost the railroad," said the engine dispatcher.

"Don't look at me," said Mr. Landsdowne. "*I* didn't call
them."

It was the wrong moment for Mr. Pickering to enter. He
stood in the doorway, yawned, and said:

"Well, Sourpuss, did the Guilford Hill pusher crew get
here all right?"

"I think," said Mr. Duveneck as he protected Mr. Pickering from the flashlights Mr. Landsdowne was throwing at
the machinist, "you better stick to helping people do railroad things you know how to do, like help me or the kid here
run engines in and out of the house."

Mr. Duveneck didn't know it then, but he had just set the
stage for the awfullest day the Riverside roundhouse was
ever going to have.

15

The next night Mr. Duveneck was still dismayed.

"I don't understand what went wrong," he said. "There was nothing in the therapy book to explain what Beershot done last night."

"Why don't we tell him he doesn't need to help others do railroad things any more?" I said. "I mean, after what happened with Mr. Landsdowne . . ."

"Let's not talk about *that*," said Mr. Duveneck.

"But Mr. Pickering is out on the turntable and he's sad. He . . ."

"He's out *where?*"

"On the turntable and . . ."

Mr. Duveneck stared out at the turntable. The look on his face stopped me.

"I don't see Beershot," he said.

"He *was* there."

"He ain't there now."

Mr. Duveneck looked worried.

"Kid, do you suppose he's actually helping me and you do our railroad things?" Worry changed to fear. Fear changed to panic. "Kid, we got to find that nut!"

Mr. Duveneck was running fast. His destination: the turntable.

But Mr. Pickering was nowhere in sight. He wasn't in the shanty or anywhere.

We stopped and stared into the night: nothing.

Darkness dominated the lonely acreage. Pools of light—the ones on the turntable, the one at the ashpit, and far away, the string of lights at the coal dock—were the only touches of life in the black. No people moved in and out of the lights. On the ashpit track on the outbound lead an engine sat, steam rising from it, and when I looked its way, the engine popped. We didn't hear the noise the engine at the ashpit made. The noise our hearts made was too loud.

"Maybe," said Mr. Duveneck, "Beershot went up to the dock. Come on, kid."

We moved fast through the cold night. As we passed the tin shanty where the Negro who built fires in locomotives or dumped ashes out of them dozed, Mr. Duveneck stopped. He shoved open the shanty door and shouted:

"Where's Beershot? You seen him?"

The gray-haired Negro, who looked like a senator, yawned and said:

"He ain't here."

"I *know* he ain't," Mr. Duveneck said. "I got eyes, ain't I? But we got to get ahold of him. Have you seen him?"

"Climb off your high horse, Duveneck," the Negro said. He was a church deacon, had seven children, wore yellow shoes, and on his night off ran a bust-out game. "He was here no more'n two minutes ago, standing exactly where you is, and talking about doing railroad things because he's got no loom for rug weaving."

"Where was he going?" said Mr. Duveneck, getting desperate.

"He don't ask me what I had for breakfast," the Negro said, "and I don't ask him."

"We got to find Beershot!"

Mr. Duveneck was trembling.

"Why go and bother him? He don't go and bother you, does he? He eats his breakfast and you eats . . ."

"Please," I said. "Where was he going?"

The Negro looked at me thoughtfully.

110

"Kid, you ain't heard a word I said. I don't ask you what you had for breakfast, do I? I . . ."

"We have to know," I said.

"I don't see how she matters . . ."

"It *matters*," I said.

"Well," he said, "this morning I had me ham, fried potatoes, and . . ."

"We don't care *what* you ate!" Mr. Duveneck shouted.

"The kid wanted to know," said the Negro, hurt.

"No," I said. "I wanted to know . . ."

"You say one thing, you mean another," said the Negro. "I got no more time to waste. Beershot should be coming down the tracks soon. He . . ."

"Coming down the tracks?" the hostler said, paling.

"Sure," said the Negro. "He went up to the dock to bring down that Pacific. I got to knock her fire. She's going in for a twelve-month card and . . ."

Mr. Duveneck was out the door like a shot and running to the docks.

But coming at him—faster—was the Pacific. I could tell by its noise that Mr. Pickering was dreaming. He was approaching too fast to stop at the ashpit and get the fire dumped. He was, instead, zeroed in on the turntable.

Mr. Duveneck and I ran up the track to the oncoming engine a quarter mile away.

Pacifics, though not as grand as Hudsons, were sweet locomotives. These were the K-3's that evolved from the K-2 and the K-1, which they first built in 1903. Their driver wheels stood more than six and a half feet high. They had boosters that increased their traction force by ten thousand pounds, which gave Mr. Pickering's Pacific the power it needed to barrel along the short, quick stretch of track between the coal dock and the turntable. Happily, the turntable tracks were lined up for the approaching monster, because Mr. Pickering had under his control two thousand horsepower —and he was dreaming. He had the throttle all the way back,

111

the Johnson bar all the way forward, and in his mind he was tooling along the water-level route somewhere between Chicago and Cleveland. In his mind he was pulling the glittering first-class coaches of the Twentieth Century Limited. He didn't see the turntable; he saw only Indiana flatland, green boards, and fat women waving aprons at him.

The sixteen-year-old Pacific, which weighed 303,000 pounds, was careening down the tracks, headed for its greatest adventure since it saw the light of day in Schenectady in 1924.

With a roar and a blur, the locomotive passed us by. Just before he reached the turntable tracks, Mr. Pickering threw the driver wheels into reverse, causing the great wheels to spin backward like wild men, but making the engine stop before it rolled off the other end of the table and ended in a patch of weeds.

"Beershot!" Mr. Duveneck shouted. *"Wait!"*

But we were too far up the track. As we ran to the table, Mr. Pickering had time to shut off the throttle, climb from the engine cab, line the table up with an empty stall, and climb back again into the engineer's seat.

We got to the table just as Mr. Pickering's hand got to the throttle.

"No!" Mr. Duveneck bellowed.

But he could not make himself heard above the engine noise.

"Wait!" I shouted.

But Mr. Pickering had eyes only for the track ahead. He didn't see the brick wall where the track ended in the roundhouse. He saw a green board and somewhere in the glimmering distance: Chicago. As soon as his hand had touched the throttle, he had been reclaimed by the dream.

Locomotives are not supposed to race into the roundhouse from the turntable; they're supposed to creep, no hurry, easy does it, safety first, and all that. But its bell dinging, its main rods in motion, steam blowing from its cylin-

112

ders, the Pacific chugged off the turntable and into the roundhouse—and each turn of its drivers made it go faster. It wasn't going lickety-split, but it was going fast enough.

Mr. Richter, the third-trick foreman, drifting along half-asleep through the house, heard the engine noise, saw the engine wasn't going to stop in time, and shouted:

"No, Beershot, no!"

Mr. Pickering, dreaming, didn't hear him, either.

Mr. Duveneck shouted:

"No, Beershot, no, no, no!"

Then he did what I did.

He put his hands over his eyes.

But, Mr. Pickering had not awakened from his dream. He was too involved with it. To him, it was Chicago or bust.

The crash was loud but beautiful.

When I uncovered my eyes I saw Mr. Duveneck racing into the roundhouse. I ran after him.

The engine, becalmed, was sticking halfway through the roundhouse wall.

It had run out of track, punched a hole in the brick, but the dirt road beyond wouldn't support its weight, so there it came to a halt: its drivers, belly, and smokestack outside; the rest inside; and everywhere lots of bricks, broken glass, and steam.

Mr. Pickering, unhurt, climbed down from the cab, inspected the situation, coughed nervously, and said:

"Uh . . . uh . . ."

The foreman, dismayed, had these words:

"Beershot, I don't think you should have done that."

"Are you all right, Mr. Pickering?" I said.

He nodded. He looked at the locomotive again as if seeing it for the first time and said:

"She's sure in there good, ain't she?"

Others assembled. They were grumpy. The crash had awakened them.

"I just don't know how she happened," Mr. Pickering said,

113

troubled. "I was pretending I was running the Flyer and there you are. That hole in the wall makes a draft in here, don't she?"

"Beershot . . ." said Mr. Duveneck. He stopped; he was beside himself, and he couldn't think of more to say.

But the foreman could.

"I think we better get that engine back where she belongs," he said. "We better do it before somebody drives along that road out there. They won't be expecting an engine in the road."

Mr. Duveneck agreed.

"I'll bring that Mohawk in behind her," he said. "Maybe we can pull her back inside."

The foreman nodded.

"Her drivers will line up okay, but her trucks are going to give us trouble. Well, we got to do something." He looked at Mr. Pickering. There was gloom in his eyes. "Beershot," he said, "the least you could have done was gotten one that had no front trucks."

There was something sad about seeing a roundhouse that way: its wall punched out and a passenger locomotive plugging the hole. Even before dawn arrived, the scene looked sad. Darkness could not diminish its awfulness.

Besides, everyone showed up; the general foreman, all the other foremen, railroad officials I didn't recognize, and a hobo off the eastbound freight. Each looked sleepy. Each when he came upon the scene shook his head in disbelief. Each looked sad.

Reports, somehow, would have to be filled out. The wall would have to be repaired. The engine's busted headlight needed fixing. But with the railroad it is first things first—and the first thing was to keep the railroad running. Later would be time enough to brood over the whys and wherefores. Railroads are equipped with *big* items: locomotives, freight cars, tons of rail, and miles of real estate. The railroad's business is big, as Mr. Duveneck said later, and "when we make

114

mistakes we make whoppers. That's the way railroading is. These ain't buttons we're playing with."

It wasn't until a week later that the board of inquiry was held to sweep the entire matter under a rug. By that time things that seemed so terrible had lost their terribleness and, as one official said, "If you don't mind I'd rather not find out *how* it happened. I'm afraid of the answers I'll get. Anyway, there's this war in Europe and labor is getting scarce. Suppose we fired the whole third trick? We'd never be able to replace them." Also, he said, "Let's keep the matter here in the division. New York would never understand. And they might cause trouble for *us*, too. We've got enough trouble now." Railroad executives, the same as all executives do, like to send nice reports to the home offices. The other reports they'd just as soon forget. I tell you this now so you'll understand why the officials that night didn't run around screaming bloody murder. They said things like, "I wonder how this event came about?" They didn't exactly say that; I'm paraphrasing. That night they sounded like Mrs. Bruce, but you get the idea: the moment was momentous, and momentous moments should be swept under rugs.

The next night Mr. Duveneck buttonholed Mr. Pickering in the locker room.

"Beershot," he said, "no more therapy. Stop helping others do railroad things."

Mr. Pickering slumped.

"I was only trying to be nice," he said. "I didn't mean . . ."

"And stay away from the turntable," said Mr. Duveneck.

"All right," said Mr. Pickering. His voice was low.

"And don't run no more engines."

"All right," said Mr. Pickering. His voice was lower.

"And don't go near the coal dock or the ashpit," said Mr. Duveneck.

"All right," said Mr. Pickering.

We hardly heard him.

Mr. Duveneck couldn't stand that.

115

"Beershot, it ain't that we don't love you," he said. His voice was gentle. "Now me and the kid don't want you going around thinking that."

Mr. Pickering, impressed with love, blew his nose with that great honking noise and slowly walked away.

⸺ 16 ⸺

The day before Christmas it snowed hard. When I mushed through the railroad yard at 11 P.M. the world was ice cold and the stars seemed close enough to touch. As I passed the yardmaster's shanty, I looked inside and saw a Christmas tree: two strands of lights, but no tinsel or ornaments. I heard the yardmaster's radio:

> *Silent night, holy night*
> *All is calm,*
> *All is bright . . .*

I passed boxcars festooned with snow, boxcars that waited in dreamless sleep for the switch engine to sort and make a train of them. But the switch engine, unattended, waited, too. Its crew was in the yard office, looking at the Christmas tree, and thinking of Christmas.

I was glad to reach the roundhouse. I stomped snow off my shoes, my teeth stopped chattering, my fingers got feeling back, and my nose stopped running. But the roundhouse was an empty place. Only a skeleton force had been scheduled. Those with seniority got Christmas off; I didn't. When I went out to the turntable to help Mr. Duveneck, I was feeling blue. I didn't want to think about Christmas or anything. It was that kind of night.

Now, there's a study for you. Mr. Duveneck was doing push-ups in the snow. It was so cold I thought a glacier had

117

come through, but Mr. Duveneck wore only what he wore in summer: overalls, shoes, socks, shirt—and that's all! He didn't wear gloves, either. I was pleased his hands were turning blue.

"Merry Christmas!" he shouted. "Want to build a snowman?"

"No. You'll catch cold," I said. "You'll . . ."

"Pores!" he beamed.

"Pores?"

"Pores," he said. "Bundle up and your pores can't breathe. Pores need air. Show me a pore with a cough and I'll show you a sick man."

"Mr. Duveneck, it's freezing out!"

"Take animals," he said. "Do they wear clothes? No. They tell their pores what to do and . . ."

"Why are your hands turning blue?" I said.

"My hands are *not* turning blue. It's the blue light in the turntable shanty that causes it," he said, pointing a blue finger at a white bulb.

"How can white light cause . . ."

"Kid, what colors do you mix to make purple?"

"Red and blue, but . . ."

"There you are! Things are not always what they seem. Bernarr Macfadden says . . ."

He would have said more, but Mr. Pickering wafted up, coughed, destroyed five snowflakes with Old Grand-Dad fumes, and said:

"Well, she's Christmas Eve. Merry Christmas, kid. Merry Christmas, Duveneck. Merry Christmas, God."

Mr. Duveneck was becalmed.

"God?"

"The whole shooting match was His idea, wasn't it?" said Mr. Pickering.

All Mr. Duveneck could say was:

"Oh boy . . . oh boy . . ."

So I said:

"Why don't we go in where it's warm?"

118

We three settled in the locker room. I don't know what the sudden warmth did to Mr. Duveneck's pores. All I know is, when he thought we weren't watching, he sneaked worried glances at his hands as they turned from blue to white to red.

Mr. Pickering pulled out his railroad watch.

"She's getting close to that time," he said.

Mr. Duveneck looked alarmed.

"You promised last year was the last," he protested.

Mr. Pickering looked sad.

"Duveneck, is you going to play softball again next summer with them kiddies?"

"They *need* me," said Mr. Duveneck. "I'm the best player they got."

"But they is only twelve."

"Guess again," said Mr. Duveneck. "One pitcher is a midget."

"But you is going to play?"

"Of course!"

"And you is going to want me to do like last summer? Sit in the stands with the daddies and shout nice things at you?"

Mr. Duveneck slammed his fist on the table.

"All right, Beershot, all right! But this is the last time! We got a railroad to run. We got no time for . . ."

"I'll bring the torches," said Mr. Pickering and drifted out of the locker room into the roundhouse.

"What's going on?" I said.

Mr. Duveneck, sulking, didn't answer. So while I waited for Mr. Pickering to return with the torches, I wondered if he planned to set fire to something. And I wondered to what. The railroad was finicky. It didn't like fires—except in locomotive fireboxes, in powerhouse furnaces, and in potbellied stoves in country depots. But everywhere was the threat of fire.

For instance, consider the torches. Fueled by kerosene they were quart cans that tapered to a snout where a cloth wick flickered. The more the wick was exposed, the brighter

119

the flame: an orange and unsteady light. Torches prevented machinists from hitting their thumbs when they hammered in the dark underneath locomotives.

Each worker on running repair had one and it was usually burning. Working in the pit on the underbelly of an engine was a wet and greasy task compounded by water dripping and darkness. If the engine had to be in and out fast, there wasn't time for its attendant to hook up an electric extension light. Anyway, torches were more dramatic. Mr. Pickering said once they had a beauty.

"When they run an engine into a dark stall, I like to sit and watch the running repair birds come through the black, each lugging a torch," he had said. "She's like church. The guys are altar guys looking for an altar to light and sing hymns about."

In a way, he was right. An engine that chugged in *hot* was the center of everyone's attention: the machinist, boilermaker, pipe fitter, their helpers, the engine inspector, the rod-cup boy, the box-packer, and—at times—the foreman. They hurried from wherever in the roundhouse they had been to where the locomotive waited. The machinist helper pushed the machinist's toolbox—a monster chest caked with crud—that rolled on two noisy iron wheels. The rod-cup boy pushed his clattering tin car that held his air-powered rod-cup gun and sticks of grease. In his wake came the box-packer, shoving his clanking cart of rattling cans of journal box oil. Behind them, pushing nothing and looking bored, came the elite: the machinist, boilermaker, engine inspector, and pipe fitter. They *all* carried torches—and *all* their torches were lighted.

Like lightning bugs trapped in a bottle, they would swarm over, under, and around the impatient locomotive, each doing his assigned job: the box-packer underneath it, the rod-cup boy beside it, the machinist in its cab, and the engine inspector everywhere, hitting the engine with his hammer and noting which pieces fell off. He looked at the rods to see if they were there, tried the brakes to hear them hiss,

watched the gauges wiggle, but mostly he checked the soft-
ness of the engineer's seat. Although he was supposed to in-
spect under each engine, it dripped there; he didn't want to
get his cap wet, so he shouted to the box-packer in the pit:

"Is everything okay?"

And the box-packer would shout back:

"I guess so."

After which, the inspector would climb into the cab,
yawn, and check the engineer's seat.

But he never let loose of his hammer and torch. It was
scary to see him in the engineer's seat, eyes closed, and dangling his hammer from one hand, and from the other, his
torch. Its flames licked at his overalls, but he never caught
fire, if that helps.

Nonetheless, consider the drums of kerosene, the vats of
paint for prettying engines, the wads of waste that dangled
from pockets, the welder's flame, the hot coals dropped from
fireboxes, and add to these items the torches carried and the
fact that the third-trick men moved in a trance—and you can
understand why the roundhouse was a fire hazard. So they
held fire drills—on the first trick.

On the first trick the powerhouse whistle would go
whoop-whoop-whoop-whoop—short, fast, and frightened
combinations, each combination indicating a different location—announcing either a drill or a fire for real. No one took
the *whoop-whoop-whooping* seriously. Those assigned to
the fire-fighting squad would throw down their tools; shout
whoop-whoop-whoop, too; and race to the fire cart: a two-
wheeled thing that contained hose and axes. The rest would
step aside fast because, as Mr. Pickering said once, there's
something unsettling about a bunch of middle-aged birds
pushing a cartful of axes and shouting *whoop-whoop-
whoop*. Each fire drill, regardless of location, ended the
same. The squad would gallop to stall twelve, the storeroom,
or the parking lot, and after bickering over who was to hook
up the hose and squirt it, the men would get the hose

hooked up and squirt water at the turntable, which made its ancient first-trick operator wet and angry.

That was the fire protection on the first trick. There was no fire squad on the third trick and the second trick didn't believe in such nonsense. Anyway, there weren't enough of us on the third trick to organize a fire squad. Also, if the powerhouse whistle *whoop-whoop-whooped* at 3 A.M., Sedamsville would have written complaining letters to the Cincinnati *Post*.

"Well, here we is."

Mr. Pickering, carrying three lighted torches and constituting a walking fire hazard, came back into the locker room.

"But remember," said Mr. Duveneck as he took a torch, "I'm no tenor. I'm a bass. Tenors is sissies."

"She's the thought that counts," Mr. Pickering said. "Here, kid. Take a torch and be a tenor."

I took a torch.

"I think I'm a bass," I said.

"We can't *all* be basses," complained Mr. Duveneck. "Be a boy soprano."

"I can't," I said. "I'm eighteen. And I'm not a soprano."

"My voice is deeper than your voice," said Mr. Duveneck.

"She's the thought that counts," Mr. Pickering repeated. But he sounded less certain.

"Well," said Mr. Duveneck, "I guess we is all basses." He gave me a dark look, though.

I had to ask.

"What's going on? What have basses and tenors got to do with these torches? Mr. Pickering, I'm confused."

"If you're confused, I better sing the melody," said Mr. Duveneck. "You harmonize."

"Harmonize to *what*?"

"To what I sing melody to, that's what," said Mr. Duveneck, getting testy. "I would have been a great singer," he added, "if I had ever learned to sing."

"Swell," I said, "but . . ."

"She's midnight, men," said Mr. Pickering. "We better go."

Mr. Pickering wafted through the door into the round-house. He carried his torch cupped in both hands in front of him. Mr. Duveneck followed, holding his torch the same way.

"Remember, kid," Mr. Duveneck said, "*I* sing the melody."

"But what's . . ."

"Follow me," he said. "She happens every year."

He walked a few steps behind Mr. Pickering, so I walked a few steps behind him. Single file, we moved along the engine stalls.

Without warning, Mr. Duveneck began to sing:

Silent night, holy night . . .

And Mr. Pickering, walking at a tilt because of Old Grand-Dad, joined in:

All is calm. All is bright . . .

So I added my voice to theirs.

Men dozing in engine cabs awoke and watched as we passed. I thought they would make fun and hoot, but they didn't. They listened and shut their eyes again. They weren't napping. They were thinking of Christmas and home.

We three moved out of the roundhouse. The tower light lighted the snowy yards as bright as day. As I brought up the rear, I watched Mr. Pickering drift around switch points and stumble over snowflakes.

Sleep in heavenly peace . . .

Mr. Pickering *believed*. The evidence of Christmas, to him, was unimpeachable. In the sky a host of angels in overcoats flew. The tower light was the star of the east. What if the shepherds tended boxcars instead of sheep and who says wise men must ride camels? Couldn't they stumble along a railroad track?

Then the Sedamsville church bells stopped ringing. Mr. Pickering—awed—stopped singing.

Without a word, he blew out his torch, turned, and shuffled by us back into the roundhouse.

I started after him, but Mr. Duveneck stopped me.

"Not now," he said.

"But . . ."

"Not now, kid."

Are all men lonely? I think they are. I know that night that Mr. Pickering and Mr. Duveneck were.

17

February afternoons in Cincinnati are cold and gray. This one was no different. I saw Kathleen shiver as she climbed off the Warsaw streetcar and as she hurried into the warmth of the Paradise. She didn't see me in the bank doorway. But I hurried to her as fast as I could. When I entered the Paradise she looked up from our booth and grinned at me. It happened that way every afternoon. We met there every day she was in school. Then, before her transfer ran out, she took a streetcar home. And I walked home to sleep.

The Paradise—or Eighth and State where the Paradise was —was not a place where happiness grew on trees. It was an intersection where many streetcar lines met and changed passengers. If Eighth and State had charm, its charm had vanished. Eighth and State was a collection of newsboys at full cry, pool halls where tough guys loitered, and shapeless women lugging shapeless shopping bags filled with day-old bread. It was a collection of rowdy taverns—ill-lighted, noisy, and beery—where waitresses never wiped the bar tops dry. It was chili parlors that smelled of grease and jukeboxes that played too loud. It was middle-aged men with tooth-picks in their mouths, standing on the corner, going no-where.

But the Paradise, smelling of milk and filled with quiet, was an ice cream parlor in the old tradition. Its air was filled with chocolate fragrance and from jars of juices came the scents of fruit flavoring. The candies in its display window were sculptured dainties enthroned on cut-glass pedestals, each with a dusty doily of its own. Though banana splits at the Paradise were grand adventures, they were dramas that few attended. The Paradise possessed a grace the neighborhood had lost. The neighborhood had changed, but the Paradise had not. Because Kathleen and I never wanted to break the spell of yesterday the Paradise maintained, we always talked in murmurs there.

"It's not working out," I murmured as I sat across from her. "I'm not going to make it."

I shoved my bankbook at her. It showed 163 dollars.

A discerning girl—wisdom in bobby socks—Kathleen could translate my mood with a glance. There was pain in her eyes.

"I make sixty-three cents an hour," I said. "A hundred and thirty dollars a month. Out of that, I pay the rent, utilities, and buy food for my mother and me. All I could save was fifteen dollars a month."

The pain in her eyes did not go away.

"Maybe a scholarship," she began, but her voice was tentative.

"It's only good if I carry a full load at the university," I said. "I'd have to quit the roundhouse. And if I quit, who pays the rent and buys the food? A part-time job won't cover it."

We sat in silence.

Through the door came the vague noises: the grinding of streetcars, the cry of newsboys, and the shriek of high school kids. For me, the February before, life had been a ball, too. My only worry had been passing math. I had liked Western Hills High School with its gym that smelled of gym shoes, its library that smelled of books, its whopper of a lunchroom that made a whopper of a din, and its a capella choir. The year I had graduated—1940—our football team won three

126

out of nine games, our basketball team won five out of sixteen, our cross-country team lost every meet, our golf team
never won a match, but the girls' hockey team was invinci-
ble. That year it rained a lot, one girl got pregnant, and in
June three hundred ninety-four of us were graduated.

But soon Kathleen's class would be graduated, and the
class after that, and after that. They'd leave and go away. I'd
never get beyond Eighth and State.

Kathleen read this in my eyes.

"A glacier came through Eighth and State two minutes
ago," she said. "It covered the world with ice. But Mr. Pickering invented fire and made the world warm again."

I said nothing.

"The glacier was cold," she said, cocked her head,
grinned, and tried to change the mood. I couldn't bear to
see her that way.

"If he can invent fire," I said, putting the bankbook away,
"so can I. I'll invent something for you, too."

"What?" she said, trying to keep the mood light.

"The alphabet," I said.

"Good!" she said. "Now invent words. Then, sentences!"
The nonsense reached her; some of the sadness went away.
"Like, 'Step to the rear of the streetcar!' and 'Now a word
from our sponsor.' With sentences Elizabeth Barrett can
write love poems to Robert Browning—and I'll send you her
carbons! I'll . . ."

She stopped, lost, buttoned up, and took her thoughts to a
secret place I couldn't reach.

"Kathleen . . ." I said, but she shook her head.

"Please," she said, pretending to dictate a letter. "Dear
Mr. Pickering. Thank you for inventing fire. Now, invent
time. Invent time or make it stop, so George and I . . ."

She couldn't go on. The handwriting was on the wall, on
my face, in my bankbook, and everywhere.

"You better go," I said, "before your transfer runs out."

"George . . ."

127

"It's late."

"All right," she said.

She gathered her books.

I didn't walk outside with her. I couldn't have stood that. I waited in the Paradise until a streetcar took her away.

18

"Say, ain't she turning nice, though?" Mr. Pickering said as we sat in the turntable shanty that first warm night.

Spring, a will o' the wisp that year, had caught us by surprise. One night the arctic winds howled against the roundhouse doors, the next night the breeze was so mellow we left the doors open. Our Siberia had gone away. But I was depressed. I pictured myself fifty springs later: a bent and wobbly old man, running the turntable and claiming it was an art.

"Well, kid," Mr. Pickering said, "next year this time you'll be in college learning things and hollering boola boola, whatever that means."

"Sure," I said but didn't mean it. I didn't have the heart to tell him he was wrong.

He snapped his fingers.

"I almost forgot," he said. "Do you suppose she'll want to do it, hating me the way she does? Still, it's been an annual event with us. And if she calls, you come along, too."

He confused me. I was going to explain boola boola.

"Go where?" I said. "And if *who* calls?"

"Rosalind," he said, "and the Whitewater."

He lumbered off the turntable, headed for the roundhouse. That was all he would say. I would have followed him to ask more details, but Mr. Duveneck was bringing a switch engine in. I couldn't desert my post.

Two nights later, after I had forgotten about it, Mr. Pickering stuck his head into the turntable shanty, woke me up, and said:

"You're in, kid! She called. So Sunday it is."

He was actually smiling.

"Sunday is *what?*"

He looked hurt.

"Rosalind," he said. "The Whitewater and spring. How come you forgot?"

"Mr. Pickering," I said, "I don't mean to be impolite, but what *are* you talking about? I think it's swell that Mrs. Bruce called you. Maybe there's hope that . . ."

"There's no hope for that," he said. "She called because it was spring."

And that was all I could get out of him.

Well, the next Sunday at seventeen minutes after seven and after most of the third-trick men had gone, I walked into the locker room and saw Mr. Pickering becalmed in front of his locker. He stared as if what he saw inside was going to bite him.

"Kid," he said, "I got me some ice-cream-colored slacks and a purply sport shirt that's a beauty. But should I wear my pink shirt that's got the pictures of dice and playing cards printed down the front of it? That one's a beauty, too."

"They both sound nice," I lied as I climbed into my street clothes. "Where you going?"

He chewed his lower lip a minute. "You mean, where is *we* going. You and me and Rosalind is going for a picnic. I been telling you about it all week. Rosalind and me do it that way every spring. She gets the biggest kick out of spring, the poor little thing." He looked grieved. "She hates my guts right now, but she wouldn't give up going for a ride in the country no more than she would give up . . . ah . . . give up . . . ah . . . well, something." He looked more grieved. "When you're a growed man," he concluded, "I got to have a man-to-man talk with you."

130

"Mr. Pickering," I said, "I thought you and Mrs. Bruce were through. I thought . . ."

"We is," he said. "According to her. But there's no one else who will take her on her annual spring picnic. That's why she called me. She'll go with me, she says, but she won't —well, we simply got to have that man-to-man talk real soon. Things is getting out of hand."

"Does she want me along, though? I'll be in the way and . . ."

"I want you along, kid." He sounded sad. "Next spring you won't be here."

"I didn't even know you had a car," I said, wanting to change the subject. "Or that you could drive."

"There is more than one way to skin a cat," he said, and added, "when you has friends."

Before he could explain, Mrs. Bruce came into the locker room and glared at us with hate, but—dressed for spring the way she was—she was a sight to see.

"My, you is pretty," Mr. Pickering said.

Well, she was *kind* of pretty. Colorful—that's a better word. Her presence filled the locker room with color and toilet-water smells. She wore a housedress that looked like a tent decorated with gaudy flowers, each trying to outshout the other. She wore a green eyeshade, white anklets that were almost clean, high-heeled shoes polished bright red, and her slip—which was showing two inches—was lined with lace, most of which was still sewed on. In honor of spring she had scrubbed her face raw, washed away the winter's accumulation of makeup, and had hurled fresh coloring at it. Her lips were mismatched gouges of red, her rouge was a powdery circle of doubt on each cheek, and her mascara— an artifice she had never mastered—made her left eye look bigger than her right one. She reeked of cologne, a pint of heady perfume, and some of the winter's sweat she had been unable to wash away. She was a gargantuan garden, colorful and scented, that had gotten out of hand, but anyway, there she was: ready to sneer hello at spring.

131

"Well," grumbled the scented garden, "I'm ready when you are, Beershot."

She focused more hate at him and added:

"But don't think you is getting any! Me and you has had it. Don't come honeying up to me because I look so sweet."

She saw me for the first time and her mood changed completely. She patted her hair, which she had forgotten to comb, and said:

"Kid, you is another matter. Me and you could . . ."

"We got to get going!" cried Mr. Pickering, mortified.

"The *kid* is going, too?"

"Yes, Rosalind. He . . ."

She cussed long and loud.

"Now more'n ever you ain't getting nothing," she whined. "You can't even hold my hand when I go wading. You ain't never learned your lesson, has you? You ain't . . ."

"I really don't think I should come along," I said. "I have other things to do and . . ."

Mr. Pickering's depression depressed me.

"It will be our last spring together, kid," he said.

He meant it one way, which was sad enough, but God meant it another, which was even sadder, but we didn't know it then.

"Come on," he said and guided us both outside the door into the fresh air. There, he stopped.

"Lend a hand, will you, kid?"

He pointed to a laundry tub of beer and ice.

"Spring makes Rosalind thirsty," he said. "But we don't have to lug it far. The freight is sitting over there, waiting."

"The freight?"

He looked embarrassed. "How else is we going to get to Valley Junction? Me and you and Rosalind is going there in the caboose."

"But that's the freight for Indianapolis," I said. "It doesn't stop between Wade and Greensburg. It . . ."

"Today," said Mr. Pickering as we approached the ca-

132

boose, "she stops at Valley Junction. She's been arranged. Here, help me lift this tub of beer aboard."

The conductor, hearing us, appeared in the caboose's back door.

"We been waiting," he complained. "Git on so we can roll. I ain't running no taxi service."

Two minutes later, we were rolling.

In case you've not had the pleasure of riding in a caboose, let me tell you how things are. They bounce too much. They're full of funny noises. They're drafty. Brace yourself one way and the caboose will lurch the other. They smell of kerosene, pipe tobacco, wet wood, steam, and leather. They're leaky. They're poorly lighted. They're nothing but toolboxes on wheels. But never say these things to a conductor; his caboose is his castle. To him, it's office, home, and sanctuary. It is the place to come in from out of the rain. It is the place to come in from out of the snow. It protects him from the howling winds and the boiling sun. It shakes, rattles, and heaves—and living in it is the same as living in a bowl an eggbeater is working at. The nicest thing you can say to a caboose is good-by to it, but never let the conductor hear you. Conductors are sentimental men. They would sooner part with their wives than their cabooses, so you get the idea. So much for conductors, cabooses, and conductors' wives.

As we sat in the caboose, which wasn't bouncing as much as most cabooses do because Mrs. Bruce was ballast, Mr. Pickering looked at me and shrugged. He was sorry, I could tell, that the conductor sulked in the cupalo. Mr. Pickering's look said, "There's nothing I can do about it" and "I wish that I was dead." Delhi, Sayler Park, and Addyston flashed by as we rattled west through the valley. Before we knew it we could hear the engineer—at the head of the train, far away—whistling through North Bend and Cleves, but he whistled an unhappy whistle and with good reason. He couldn't race through the valley to build up speed for Guilford Hill because, at Valley Junction at the start of the hill, he had to stop where he wasn't supposed to, and let us off.

Guilford Hill, that climb from the Ohio River Valley to the flatland plateau of Indiana, was the cross men on the Indiana division had to bear. There was no other way, on that division, to reach Indianapolis and points beyond, except up that awful hill. Sometimes pusher engines were used; even they didn't help much. The hill hated every train that came along and slowed it to a crawl. That stretch between Valley Junction—actually Lawrenceburg Junction three miles west of Valley Junction—to Sunman, Indiana, at the top of the hill was main-line track that snaked around and sometimes seemed to climb straight up. Passenger trains, including the ones they double-headed, started out fast but ended in a creep up that awful, awful hill. Like giants in slow-motion they labored up the terrible grade, crawling painfully through Ross, Bonnell, and Weisburg as if each turn of their drivers would be the last and their red-hot hearts might explode. The angry hill played no favorites. It reduced Hudsons, Mohawks, and Pacifics to dime-store toys of no consequence. That was going *up* the hill; coming down was worse.

Coming down into the Ohio Valley was a nightmare blur of noise. It was a freewheeling ride on an idiot roller coaster that hurled without good sense around curves—and there was always a tighter curve ahead. Mile-markers seemed to flicker by with the *pish-pish-pish* of telephone poles. Heavy-bottomed passenger cars pushed the engine down, down, down. Oil, sloshing wildly in a tank-car train, pushed and sloshed and the engineer seemed to have no control; all he could do was ride it out and wait for the bottom of the hill to come. His engine cab bucketed and swayed, became a violent thing with a mind of its own. To ride a rudderless ship into a gale would have been smoother, and that was Guilford Hill, the cross the Indiana division had to bear.

The engineer who ran our freight was bearing it in anger. He was fed up. He had wanted to make a run for Guilford Hill and, perhaps, this time conquer it, but no, he had to stop at Valley Junction, let us off, start from scratch, and hope for the best.

"It ain't the way we like to railroad," muttered the conductor.

"Aw," said Mr. Pickering. "You'll make her up the hill nice. I got faith in you."

"You better have faith in the engine we got," the conductor said. His voice was gloomy. "I hear she's due for a carding and her boilers ain't been washed in months."

"Don't worry about her," Mr. Pickering said. "She's a good engine. I fixed her main rods once. And I fixed her brakes once. And I put new brass in her. Seems like every time she comes in, she needs fixing. And her injector is shot. I don't think her cylinder heads has been tightened since . . ." He stopped. He looked at the conductor, worried. "Come to think of it," he concluded, "I think you're being pulled by a jinx. I'm surprised she made it this far."

The conductor, shaken, said:

"Well, here you are at Valley Junction."

"Swell," said Mr. Pickering.

"Have a good time, ma'am, up the Whitewater," the conductor said to Mrs. Bruce. He had once worked passenger and had never gotten it out of his system.

Mrs. Bruce sneered at him.

"Up *your* Whitewater!" she bellowed.

The freight whistled in its flag and off it went to try Guilford Hill. It didn't seem too inspired, though, as it chugged away; and the conductor, standing on the caboose's back porch, seemed upset about what Mrs. Bruce had said to him. Then the freight was gone and we were standing by the Valley Junction tower.

The towerman, troubled, looked down from his second-floor window. He had not expected the freight to stop or passengers to get off. He had, actually, been expecting an easy Sunday, sitting in his Morris chair, listening to the click of the telegraph and the ring of the telephone and knowing neither clicked nor rang for him. But there was that *look* in his eyes. The look said, "Somehow I should have stood in bed."

"Beershot," he called, "you mean she's spring already?"

"She sure is," said Mr. Pickering.

"Well," said the towerman, "there she sits."

He pointed to the speeder.

Mr. Pickering walked over to it—that little, motorized track car painted yellow—checked its fuel supply, seemed satisfied, set its controls, and began to crank the crank that would start the gasoline engine.

"Can I help?" I said.

"I wish you would, kid," he said. "Every year these birds get crankier."

There was an explosion and we were surrounded by fumes. The noise was shattering, but the gasoline engine was going.

"There!" said Mr. Pickering. He was pleased. "Can you keep her perking till I get back?"

"Sure, but . . ."

"I'll be right back. Don't you worry none."

Of course, what we were doing was against all rules. The speeder wasn't a toy; it wasn't to play with. The speeder was assigned to the trackwalker, who didn't walk; he rode. It was assigned, also, to the section crew who fiddled with the right-of-way. They tightened track bolts, replaced rail, tamped ballast, and threw rocks at rabbits. But on Sundays the trackwalker stayed home and rested his feet, and the section crew got drunk on cheap wine. Not all of them got drunk, I mean, but enough of them got drunk to make life a challenge. Hangovers, though, didn't slow them down. On Mondays—their heads splitting—they swung sledges with a ferocity a track machine will never know.

Well, I was sitting on the speeder, caught up in its noise, and I didn't see Mr. Pickering and the towerman until they were practically next to me. They manhandled the towerman's Morris chair across the siding track. They said things to each other like:

"Easy there!"

"Watch her!"

"You got ahold?"

"No, ain't you?"

"Watch my fingers!"

And,

"Oops!"

After much exertion, they put the Morris chair on one of the peanut-sized flatcars that speeders pull.

"Beershot," said the towerman, "you just shot my Sunday to smithereens. I'm sick and tired of this happening every spring. For one thing, it ain't legal. You ain't supposed to fool with that speeder. For another, you ain't supposed to ride her up the valley. Suppose somebody catches you? It'd be my hide, not yours. And another thing: that's a good chair there, only each time you bring her back, she's squashed down terrible and don't sit right. Beershot . . ."

Mrs. Bruce shoved him aside with a wave of her fat hand and climbed up on the little flatcar, settled with a whoosh into the Morris chair, kicked off her high-heeled shoes, sprawled out and waggled her toes, adjusted her green eye-shade, and commanded:

"All right! All right! Hand up that tub of beer. Does a lady have to do everything herself!"

Without a word, Mr. Pickering and the towerman hoisted the tub aboard the flatcar. She grabbed a cold one, opened it, drank, belched, and said to the towerman:

"Well, you getting much?"

"I think you better go," the towerman said to Mr. Pickering. He was blushing.

He helped Mr. Pickering hook the flatcar to the speeder. While he did, he stole glances at Mrs. Bruce.

"Lord," he said, "she's an immense one, ain't she?"

"Well, kids," he called one minute later, as he threw the switch that switched us off the main line to Indianapolis and on to the branch line turnout, "have fun up the White-water!"

137

"Up *your* Whitewater!" Mrs. Bruce bellowed.

The towerman blushed again.

Disconcerted, Mr. Pickering climbed on to the speeder beside me, vaguely adjusted the controls, and—three back-fires and a cloud of smoke later—the speeder began to roll along the tracks, pulling behind it the flatcar on which, glaring hatefully at the world, Mrs. Bruce was enthroned.

We swung off the main line, crossed U.S. 50, and there we were: putt-putting up the single track of the Whitewater Valley branch.

"Actually," said Mr. Pickering above the engine's racket, "I needed you for weight. With just me on this poor little thing, there ain't enough weight to hold her to the track and pull what we is pulling. The wheels keep spinning." He smiled with hesitation. "It's all right, ain't it? I mean, things is going to work out fine." He looked back at Mrs. Bruce. "Is everything all right?" he called.

She made a comment not important to the story—and the spring junket had officially begun.

The Whitewater Valley branch—those 50.8 miles of Toonerville Trolley track between Valley Junction and Connersville, Indiana—is a shy little Tinker-Toy railroad that plays hide-and-seek with the highways. It follows the road for a while, grows embarrassed—or perhaps frightened by a half-pint grade—and drifts quietly from sight to hide behind a stand of corn or sneak through a small-scale gorge. It creeps away, you think it's gone for good, but unexpectedly there it is again, running beside the highway as if it had never left at all. And then away it goes again.

Commuter trains—from Connersville and Brookville—used to travel these tracks: streaking across the back ends of cornfields, hiding in the woods, rattling across rickety wooden trestles, and whistling hello to a thousand dirt-road crossings that crisscrossed the valley; but that was long ago. Now only one freight a day makes the junket: up each morning, back each night, and Sundays nothing runs; the right-of-way dozes.

From the cab of an engine, or the speeder Mr. Pickering and I rode, a ride through the Whitewater Valley is a ride on all the toy trains from all the amusement parks combined. First, it's single track. Trees, weeds, and fences close in on you. Second, there's no straightaway. The track curves, twists, turns, and curves again: dodging this rise, avoiding that hog house; sometimes seeking the woods and sometimes seeking the sun. Go around a curve, anticipate wilderness, and a village comes up to surprise you. You pass along its backyard fences and, just as suddenly, the village is gone as if it had never been. There are no cities in that valley, only villages, each smaller than the rest. They're tucked in Lilliputian hollows or hidden in stands of trees that date back to the Indians. For instance you'll pass Cedar Grove. It has no more than two hundred people; the map makers give it the smallest typeface they have. There's Metamora: a few people more but the same size type. There's Laurel. Now, *there's* a big town: more than five hundred people and a tumbledown bandstand in its tumbledown park. I must be honest. There is Brookville and Harrison. The railroad sneaks through the backs of these towns. Each has more than a thousand people. These towns dominate the valley. But so it goes, all the way up the track. Each town has a depot and —except for Connersville—the depots are closed. Their windows are busted and grass grows where the platforms used to be. The valley's love affair with the railroad is fading, and —to be correct—it was not so hot in the first place.

"She used to be a busy branch," Mr. Pickering said. "Only something happened. I don't know what."

"The canal went bust, too," I said.

He nodded.

We chugged along on the speeder and could still see traces of the canal. Before the railroad serviced the valley, a canal had connected Cincinnati with Cambridge City, Indiana. But when the canal stopped running (it was never much of a success), the railroad put its tracks on what used to be the towpath, and that was that. Some of the canal locks still stand: crumbling stonework captured by weeds; and in certain stretches, water still flows in the canal—and they say the fishing is good. It wasn't the canal's or railroad's fault that the valley died a little each time; time did that. Farms got bigger, villages got smaller, and young people went away. Was it the canalboat that carried them off, the railroad, or a Hupmobile? Well, whatever took them, took them; they're gone, and what's left are frame houses that are falling down and retired farmers sitting in little villages, cutting grass, raking leaves, and waiting for God's whisper.

It's a moody valley. Don't be fooled by its silence. When thunder breaks the silence, the noise scares the pants off railroad men. Thunder means rain—and rain means washouts. Then it's the New York Central System versus the Whitewater River. The river always wins round one. Sometimes the railroad wins round two. After that, both wait for more thunder and more rain to see who wins again. Sometimes entire sections of track have slipped down into the river. Sometimes a freshet comes along, flows a sneaky way, washes the roadbed out from under the crossties and the rail, and leaves them dangling in the air, good for nothing but gaping at.

But it wasn't raining that Sunday, there was no thunder, and the only thing that threatened the calm of the valley was Mrs. Bruce.

I got a big kick out of her that day. Sprawled in that Morris chair, her green eyeshade low over her eyes, she was a sloppy queen on a bumpy throne. When the flatcar swayed, her fat swayed. When the flatcar bounced, her fat bounced. When it clattered over switch points, her chins shook. Now and then she would bend over, fish out a cold bottle of beer from the tub, open the bottle, drink from it, belch a belch that frightened sparrows, wipe her mouth with the back of her hand, drink again, belch again, wipe again—and hurl the empty bottle at a tree, nailing nature each time, not missing once.

Sometimes she shouted above the speeder's noise:

140

"Can't you make this thing go faster!"

Once she ripped off her eyeshade and squinted into the woods.

"Hey," she brayed. "There's some squirrels doing it!"

Galvanized by nature, she watched until they were out of sight.

"She likes animals," Mr. Pickering said. He looked desperate. "But she is a loudmouth, ain't she?"

I sneaked a look at her while she was sneaking looks at a bull in a field.

In her green eyeshade Mrs. Bruce was a single-minded and outlandish woods nymph. Her stares made a parody of nature. With stony looks she turned nature inside out to satisfy her whopping needs. But she saw only the jigsaw pieces of spring's puzzle; she never once saw the picture the pieces made. She was forever an earthy woman—fat and sneering —who didn't like the way trees mated (their method seemed dull to her) or frogs made love (she wondered what fun that was). What she was, really, when it came to sex, was a heavy-duty fundamentalist. In her mind, she wasn't warped; it was the woods that were.

"You mustn't think ill of Rosalind," Mr. Pickering said as if he had read my mind. "Somewhere inside her, there's a lot of good."

"Where?" I said.

"I ain't found it yet," he said.

It was impossible to argue with him. He never argued back.

Eighteen miles, sixteen beers, five squirrel matings, and three hog couplings down the track, the speeder bumped into Cedar Grove. The tracks pass in back of Cedar Grove where, if Cedar Grove had had an industrial section, the industrial section would have been.

Mrs. Bruce, dozing, awoke with a start when Mr. Pickering blew the Klaxon horn for a crossing. She glared about hatefully.

141

"What jerky dump is this?" she bawled and opened another beer.

Mr. Pickering pretended she hadn't spoken.

"How many people they got in this dump?" she shouted. She could be heard for miles.

To quiet her, Mr. Pickering said:

"More'n two hundred."

"If they'd do it more," she announced, "they'd have a real big city!"

A woman looked from a kitchen window; she had not seen a sight like Mrs. Bruce before.

"Honey," Mrs. Bruce bellowed to her, "you got to do it more! All you broads here have got to do it more!"

By this time Cedar Grove was behind us. Mrs. Bruce, city planner, snorted with satisfaction.

"At least," she shouted to us, "the pigs here has got the idea. I seen two of them back there that was . . ."

"Sometimes," said Mr. Pickering to me fast, "Rosalind gets too enthused. I hope that lady back there understood. You know what I mean."

"Sure," I said. "I wasn't born yesterday."

"Don't talk dirty," he said.

He stared ahead and added:

"Watch for Brookville. She should be coming up soon. She's six miles up the track."

For the hundredth time the track swung away from the road and headed for the woods. We passed a pint-sized hill and the civilized world vanished. Alongside the track, the Whitewater River trickled. It was wide at that point, but only inches deep.

"*Stop here!*" commanded Mrs. Bruce. "This here spot is as good as any. We is out of sight of the road, houses, and everything."

Mr. Pickering slowed the speeder, stopped it, shut off the gasoline engine, and the silence was a relief. I could hear birds singing, cars humming along an unseen highway, and the water splashing against the rocks in the riverbed.

142

Mrs. Bruce climbed down from her flatcar, walked up to us, and said:

"Spring sure makes me horny."

She glanced at me.

"Don't spring make you horny, kid?"

"*Rosalind!*" stammered Mr. Pickering. He was undone. "You shouldn't . . ."

That riled her.

"I wasn't going to hurt him," she shouted. A load lifted from my mind. "What's the good of spring anyway," she complained. "You can't and he don't know how. What's the use of watching squirrels and pigs doing it? What's *wrong* with doing it? Answer me *that*, Beershot! *Doing it makes babies. Doing it is . . .*"

She stopped!

Recollection overwhelmed her, her anger fled, and only anguish was left, and remembering.

She cursed, but it was a hollow curse.

She turned, not daring to look at us, and walked to the water's edge. She walked slow, so slow. She plopped down on the ground, removed her anklets, hiked up her flowered housedress, waded into the shallow water, and just stood, her back still to us. That was all. Maybe she was crying. Maybe she wasn't. We had no way of telling. All I know is, watching her, I felt sorry for her.

"Is she okay?" I said.

Mr. Pickering looked worried.

"Spring tears her to pieces," he said.

"Should we go to her?"

He shook his head.

"She'll work her way out of it," he said. "She always does, the poor little thing . . ."

So we sat and listened to the water slurp and gurgle. We smelled the moist of spring and the rot that winter had left behind. We watched birds fly, some with twigs in their mouths. We watched a line of ants march single file up a

143

tree. It was sunny where we sat, warm, silent, and dreamy, too.

I forgot about Mr. Pickering and Mrs. Bruce. It was that kind of a day. I thought about Kathleen. I pictured her, years from then, dating some rich guy, looking at him as she looked at me before, and getting married to him. I pictured their car driving away from the church; everybody threw rice at it and tin cans were tied to its back bumper. I pictured them driving along River Road—the ribbons on their car, her inside in white, and the noise the tin cans made—and there I was, standing at Delhi Avenue, holding my lunch box, waiting to go to work. They passed, they didn't look; she was looking at him, they were gone, and she hadn't seen me at all.

I wanted to say to Mr. Pickering, "Listen. Spring is tearing me to pieces, too."

But I couldn't. One look at him stopped me. There he was: forty-six springs to his credit and not a vintage spring in the lot. If I had said to him, "Listen, Mr. Pickering, there isn't going to be any college. I'm fresh out of cash. I've got to be like you and like my father was . . ." what would he have said back? He would have said, "Don't worry, kid, she'll work out. Things always do." And I would have said, "When will they work out for you!" and *that* would have hurt him more than any man was meant to be hurt.

So I said nothing.

Mrs. Bruce, who had wandered somewhere downstream and around a bend, broke the silence of the woods when she began to sing "Springtime in the Rockies." She sang it in anger, she didn't sing it well, she had no choir voice, but she sang it, and somehow she sounded free—and I was glad for her.

Mr. Pickering, dozing, also found peace in her wailing.

But, abruptly, her singing stopped.

"Beershot!" she shouted. "Two fishing worms is doing it. Come and see!"

He struggled up.

144

"You wait here, kid," he said—and looked pleased. "This happens every spring. No peeking now."

He dusted off the seat of his slacks and wandered—with hope, with misgiving, with wonder—out of sight to where she waited. His purpose was to answer the call of the wild, wherever it lay. The singing of the birds came to the Whitewater Valley and the voice of the turtle was heard in our land.

Twilight . . . and the ride back was tranquil.

Mrs. Bruce, a gray mass in a Morris chair, slept and swayed as the flatcar swayed. Mr. Pickering strained his eyes at the track ahead in the gathering darkness. He had been silent for so long.

"Are things all right now?" I had to ask. "Between you and Mrs. Bruce, I mean."

He didn't say a word.

We rode back through Cedar Grove.

"Are they?" I asked. "Mr. Pickering, what's wrong?"

He blew his nose with that great honking noise. He wiped his eyes.

"Might as well tell you," he said. "When I reached her there, it wasn't like before. She—she . . ."

He stared at the first star.

"She made fun of me," he said. "She just sat there and made fun of me."

"Mr. Pickering . . ."

"No," he said. "It's okay. It was just that I had hoped and . . . well, it's okay, kid. It's okay. She don't mean harm . . ."

The birds should have stayed out of the Whitewater Valley and that turtle should have kept his big mouth shut.

If there is an agony to spring—and there is—it is that spring exists.

145

With the world hip-deep in gloom and Mr. Pickering and me basket cases of melancholy, I began staring at each locomotive in the roundhouse as if asking it, "Did you know my father, too?" I was sure missing him that spring. I used to sit in the engine cabs and pretend he was still alive: that we were highballing through a terrible night, that he was leaning out the window checking switch points, and—this is important—that now and then he'd wink at me.

That's why, five days after our spring trip with Mrs. Bruce, while I was hooking the direct steam line to a yard engine's blowoff cock, I was touched real deep when Mr. Pickering—primed with Old Grand-Dad—floated by, stopped, yawned, and said:

"Well, that's her, the last engine your old man fired."

There was a lump in my throat as big as any lump of coal.

"I remember the morning he climbed off her," Mr. Pickering went on. "Him and me chewed the fat awhile, then he went home and died."

At last I had found *the* engine.

It was the dinkiest locomotive the division had, an o-6-o switcher built in 1912, an eighty-one ton small fry equipped with fifty-eight inch drivers, too big a cab, too small a tender, and a penny whistle to shriek at crossings with. A midget in the company of Hudsons and Pacifics, it was a leaky, hand-me-down from yesterday that time had turned into a dwarf; but, to me, no rolling stock would ever compare. It had been the last locomotive to know my father's touch.

"I'll never forget that day," Mr. Pickering said. "It was the day Winston Churchill took office."

I remember that my mother and father, the night before, were sitting in the kitchen, drinking coffee and listening to the "First Nighter." Their whole evening had been planned. After that, they would hear "We, the People," "Fibber Mc-Gee and Molly," Bob Hope, and go to bed. They spent every Tuesday evening that way. Me, I was half listening to the radio and half reading about the awfulness of Dunkirk when Mr. Landsdowne, the callboy, pounded on the front door and, not waiting for an answer, shouted:

"You're called! You're called!"

My father went to the door, he and Mr. Landsdowne talked, and Mr. Landsdowne hurried away. He had two other crews to call and time was running out.

While my father climbed into his overalls, made his red handkerchief snug around his neck, and fastened bicycle clips to his overall legs to keep the cinders out, my mother concentrated on his lunch box, which waited on the table. She brought the coffee to a boil, filled his thermos (he called it an "Icy-Hot"), made sandwiches, wrapped a slab of pie, put pickles in the lunch box, and secured the lid on the thermos. It was pretty routine for both of them, when you get right down to it. Once in high school, when I wrote an essay describing my mother and father, a real sophisticated guy complained that I had turned them into soap-opera characters. He was right, though. They *were* like soap-opera people; they were uncomplicated, they loved each other, they showed it, and they talked mostly about uncompli-cated things. My trouble is, I was taught that respecting par-ents was fashionable and I was too busy respecting them to reject them.

Anyway, when the lunch box was packed, calm returned to the kitchen, more coffee was poured, and the three of us sat around the kitchen table, talking and listening to the first

147

part of "We, the People." During the commercial, my father looked at his railroad watch and said:

"Well, it's about that time."

He winked at me, which was our good-by, kissed my mother, went out the door, and was gone.

My father spent his last night on earth in the Cincinnati bottoms, shoveling coal into that switcher's firebox as the engine sorted reefers of fruit and vegetables for this produce house and that. The engine inched through streets where trucks were kings. Piled everywhere were crates of melons, lettuce, apples, pears, and cabbages. The scent of them made the hot night moist and sweet.

The produce district was a topsy-turvy symphony of shouts: half of them Italian, all of them unintelligible. Cursing men cursed cursing men and manhandled crates and shoved carts that had four wheels. Busted melons, bruised bananas, rotting lettuce, and other discards of the harvest were tossed aside to be harvested by old men with old pushcarts in search of luxury. The area was at full cry and my father's engine—dribbling water, snorting cinders—added to the din. The engine dinged its bell, popped steam with frustration, and tooted pardon-me's at trucks that blocked its path. The trucks, unimpressed, answered with honks of contempt—and sometimes a backfire or so. My father's last night on earth had been both clangorous and full of beauty.

"What I'm trying to say," Mr. Pickering said carefully, "is I was the last bird to *talk* with your old man."

I hesitated, afraid to ask, but it had to be said:

"What did you talk about?"

Mr. Pickering looked away.

"You," he said and added quickly, "Old men is always talking about their kids. I mean, that's the way it should be."

And that was that.

I remember once when I was twelve that my father stopped an engine right in back of our house, tooted its whistle, and called me out. The engineer (I forget who he was)

was grinning at me as my father leaned out of the cab and called above the engine's noise:

"Come on! Take a ride with us!"

I was over the fence like a shot, sitting in front of my father on the fireman's seat before anyone could change his mind, then the engine was chugging along the track, and my father was saying:

"We're running light to Lawrenceburg Junction. Thought you'd like to come along . . ."

I wouldn't have traded that day for gold. Running light means there was only the locomotive. Well, I watched the needles wiggle in the gauges, watched my father open injectors to add water to the boiler, and listened to him call out green boards and switch points to the engineer. The noise inside that cab was loud and stunning. We rattled along the roundhouse lead, passed Sedamsville, and at Wade lingered on a siding because we couldn't go out on the main without written train orders from the man in Wade tower.

Some junction points, as Wade is, are in the city, but others—my father said—sit isolated along wilderness rights-of-way and these—he said—arc the loneliest. The towerman, the only human being for miles, is a castaway. Inside his tower is the constant ringing of the telephone and the constant ticking of the telegraph. But, unless the telephone rings a special ring or the telegraph ticks a special click, they are not calling him. In fact—my father said—the only chance such a towerman got to chew the fat was when a trackwalker appeared. Mostly the trackwalker came in to get warm, get a drink, or go to the toilet. Even then, the visitor didn't linger long. He went, and the towerman was alone again with the wind.

"They lead lonely lives," my father said as we waited at Wade for our orders.

After he said that, he patted my shoulder three times—as if we shared a secret women would never know.

At Wade, though, things were different. The junction was near River Road. The towerman was of the world. When things got dull—and they never did at Wade—he could lean out the window and watch the pretty girls going by on streetcars that passed inches from his building.

Finally the towerman had our orders written, went to a battery of levers that lined one wall, selected one, pulled it, and—via a crazy plumbing job—a pipe moved, caused other pipes to move until somewhere along the track a switch was reset and somewhere in the sky a railroad semaphore adjusted itself. The towerman came out, held the written train orders on a long fish pole, and waited for the engine to come by.

"Green board," my father shouted.

"Green board," repeated the engineer to show that he had heard.

The engineer eased back on the throttle and, moments later, the engine began to move.

"What did my father say about me that night?" I asked Mr. Pickering.

"It wasn't night," said Mr. Pickering. "She was morning. Four o'clock, I think, and . . ."

"You know what I mean."

Mr. Pickering looked troubled.

"He said he loved you," Mr. Pickering said.

I know, I know . . . It was in the way he put his arm on mine as the engine, running light, moved out on to the main. It was a three-mile run from Wade to Anderson Ferry, pacing River Road all the way, the Ohio River on our left, and on our right the two hundred feet high bluffs that locked us in the valley. That three mile stretch was an easy run. It curved this way and that to follow the curves of the river. Lawrenceburg Junction—and that awful Guilford Hill—were thirteen miles ahead of us. Our engine had a lot of wobbling, rocking, and heaving to do before we reached that point.

The locomotive bumped along with thumpity-thumps. My father said there was nothing to worry about. The engine wasn't falling apart. He said the pistons were connected to

150

the drivers a quarter turn apart and this made the engine sound out of balance. "This is how they *all* are," he shouted in my ear. Locomotives weren't the easiest riding contraptions: their engine boilers—long and rigid—had no "give" to them and couldn't slither around curves. They groaned and rattled around them and made the engine deck heave and rock as if we were on the deck of a ship in a gale.

But I liked to watch my father work. He checked the water glass, the steam gauge, and now and then clanked open the firebox door and looked inside to see how the fire was doing. With sea legs he strolled about the engine cab as if it were standing still. Sometimes, when the track curved to the left, he'd lean out the fireman's side, squint ahead, and shout "Crossing clear!" to the engineer, who couldn't see around the front of the engine to see what the future was.

My father was tapping my arm and pointing.

"Look," he shouted.

We were chugging by St. Vincent De Paul church with the statue out front of St. Christopher and the Christ-Child.

"I get a boot out of that," my father shouted in my ear. The cab noise was too thunderous for chitchat. "You used to crawl in *my* arms that way."

He turned his attention to the firebox. It didn't need attention. He had said more to me than he had intended to say. But neither of us had time to feel embarrassed. The engineer was blowing the whistle for the road that crossed the tracks at Anderson Ferry.

The whistle had a different tone: it bawled a nightmare noise at the crossing ahead. There was panic in its warble as it screamed. I couldn't bear to look at my father. I knew what I would see in his eyes. I would see death.

"Kid," Mr. Pickering said, "I had a feeling your old man knew he was going to die."

I didn't answer. Sometimes Mr. Pickering got too deep for his—or my—good.

151

"I mean," said Mr. Pickering, "you got to admit your old man has been around a lot where death was . . ."

Yes, Mr. Pickering. My father had been around death and was, at times, its agent. This is true of all railroad men who stare at crossings ahead.

The crossing at Anderson Ferry was dangerous. Only two months before, when my father had been firing a second section of a passenger, an automobile had tried to beat the train to that crossing—and everyone in the car (one father, one mother, three children, one dog) was killed. That night my father had come home stricken. His face was white; he couldn't talk, and he didn't have to. We had heard of it on the radio. He went into the front room and just sat. He couldn't bear to look at Mother or at me.

And, being human, that night he got drunk.

But it didn't help. He couldn't get drunk enough; no man could. So he stopped trying. The debris that death smears on the front of locomotives is easy to scrape away. The debris it leaves in the human heart never quite goes away. Each engineman has his own nightmare stretch of track. *Here a child was chopped in half. There a drunk was burned alive. Beyond that curve, a family was chewed to pieces. I remember this bridge . . . this mile-marker, this awful mile-marker, this was where it happened . . . I seen the car coming, it should have stopped, it didn't stop, and I couldn't . . . I stopped two car-lengths too late, but I couldn't stop before . . . What was they thinking of . . . When I walked back down the track, listen, I was crying . . . She was fifteen years ago, but I still wake up and hear the screams . . . At this mile-marker . . . At that turnout . . . The crossing west of town . . . Everywhere, everywhere . . . and remembered . . .*

That's why the engineer whistled in despair at the ferry crossing. That's why I couldn't look at my father.

And that's why, once past it, my father and the engineer relaxed.

We were in open country then, swinging north with the

valley. River Road kept pace with us, but below the ferry—
remember—the houses are fewer, and sometimes there are
none. Then the engineer was whistling for a string of crossings that meant the engine would be rattling through the
last of incorporated Cincinnati: Delhi, Sayler Park, and
Fernbank, the *nice* part of the world, remember? The New
York Central station in Sayler Park flashed by but its agent
didn't wave. An engine running light meant nothing to him.
He and his station had been left to die. He waited out his
years recalling when trains did stop, but the old days, as
last year's leaves, can be consumed by time and blown
away, just dust. My father said he sat in that station and did
little business, listened to the clicker clicking and the telephone bell, saying hello to children who came by, and sat
in the sun: remembering days when youth was sweet, the
world was young, and the telephone rang for him.

Edging away from the highway, the locomotive clanged
into a thicket, crossed a bridge of stone, and Cincinnati was
behind us. Addyston was coming at us down the track. The
New York Central tracks passed through Addyston under a
hill littered with makeshift shanties where Negroes lived.
Addyston's main street wasn't any prettier, but Addyston
was quick to get through and before I could feel sorry for it,
we were whistling through North Bend.

At North Bend the New York Central tracks swing west,
the Ohio River swings south, so we said good-by to the river.
North Bend was as far north as the Ohio River got, which—
my father said—is why they called it North Bend. I could
see the park on top of a hill. The park is where they buried
President Harrison. His tomb is marked by a stone column
people can see for miles. I saw a stern-wheel towboat on the
river and the smoke from its whistle, but the locomotive
noise was too loud; I couldn't hear the boat's whistle. My
father said riverboats whistled as they rounded North Bend
and the grave.

"For the memory of the President buried there," he
shouted in my ear.

153

And you, Father? Do boats whistle for you? Do crossing lights flash in your memory and do powerhouse whistles blow salutes? Or is your monument an 0-6-0 that will someday know the welder's torch?

"It ain't," said Mr. Pickering, "that railroading is wrong. It's just that I was the last bird that talked to your old man, which makes it a kind of trust. Actually, I never give her much thought till you showed up to work here, but, kid, your old man didn't want you railroading. Somehow I got to convince you to get out of here. I mean, you got no old man to tell you, so I got to do the telling. He didn't want you here. The last thing he said in this world was 'You'll never see my boy railroading.' Then he said good night, and walked up the track . . ."

. . . And through the May dawn, through Sedamsville which slept, along River Road where no one was, onto our front porch, sat on our porch swing, closed his eyes, and the Angel of Death said:

"You're called! You're called!"

I remember him on the porch swing that way; dead. He had died sitting upright, wearing his dirty overalls, his red handkerchief still around his neck, the bicycle clips still around his ankles, and my mother—sobbing—was rubbing his hands, but what was the use? His hands were cold.

A streetcar passed as the life squad came and from the streetcar window passengers stared. The streetcar slowed, moved on, was gone. Everything was over, and a fireman from the life squad said:

"There's nothing we can do. He went sudden, I would say."

They carried his body into the house, put it on a sofa, covered it with a blanket, and went away. Sedamsville was waking up. Neighbors came. The telephone didn't stop ringing. The funeral director arrived and then his crew, who took my father's body away. I felt grief but I couldn't cry. I wonder why that was? My mother cried, but I didn't cry

154

once that day. I *should* have cried. It seemed ungrateful and impolite not to.

I remember that Kathleen called me, talked, expressed sympathy, was sad, but I could only recite back ordinary words as if my father's death held no importance.

"There are neighbors here," I remember telling her. "And the funeral is scheduled for Thursday."

"I'll get Daddy to drive me right up and . . ."

"No, Kathleen."

"But . . ."

"No."

"All right, George. But can I call you later?"

"I'll call you," I said and hung up.

I didn't need her. I didn't need anything. I just stood around and waited for that awful moment when apathy would end and, as a wounded animal does, I would find a dark cave, hide, and give the tears inside me permission to use my eyes.

I realized that Mr. Pickering was staring at me, worried. I guess I had been silent for a long time.

"Kid," he said, "if you wasn't a kid, I'd give you a shot of Old Grand-Dad."

He blew his nose: again that great honking noise.

"But you *are* a kid," he said. "And you got to get out of the roundhouse."

He didn't say more; he shuffled away.

Get out of the roundhouse? Yeah, big deal. I sat on the bumper step of that dinky switcher and watched Mr. Pickering depart. Then I climbed up into the cab, sat on the fireman's side, pretended that my father was still alive, that we were highballing through a terrible night, that he was leaning out the window checking switch points, and—this is important—that now and then he'd wink at me.

20

Kathleen, Mr. Pickering, Mr. Duveneck, and I got off the streetcar at Fifth and Vine streets, walked east to Broadway, turned right, and headed to the Ohio River public landing. By the time we had gone down the hill between Fourth and Third streets, we could hear the calliope playing "Happy Days Are Here Again" and the sidewalks were crowded with other people in holiday attire headed for the public landing, too. The crowd moved down the sloping cobblestones of the landing to the wharf boat through which the people would pass to board the most beautiful excursion boat the Ohio River had ever seen: the "Island Queen."

"Uh . . . uh . . ." said Mr. Pickering as he ushered us aboard. "Don't nobody pay. This here is on me."

"Thank you," said Kathleen.

"Mr. Pickering," I said. "You really don't have to . . ."

"Shut up, kid," said Mr. Duveneck. "He's paying. That's why I came."

Anyway, there we were in the middle of July, the morning was hot and bright, and the "Island Queen" was waiting to transport us ten miles upstream to Coney Island.

As Mr. Pickering might have said it, the months of May and June had been birds. The day after Kathleen got her high-school graduation ring, President Roosevelt demanded a seven-day defense week. Three nights later I tried to tell

Mr. Pickering that I was trapped forever in the roundhouse, he was too drunk to understand, and Hamilton County set its June draft quota for nine hundred. When I tried to tell Mr. Pickering again on May 25, he was still involved in Old Grand-Dad, and the next day the British sank the "Bismarck." In June, Kathleen graduated from high school, Mrs. Bruce was seen riding in a red convertible with a B&O brakeman, Roosevelt closed the Nazi consulates, Mr. Duveneck tried to teach the third trick close-order drill, no one showed up for his lessons, and the Nazis advanced one hundred and twenty miles into Russia. On Sunday, July 6, Kathleen and I had a long, sad talk; she got exasperated; and the first parking meters appeared the next day in Cincinnati. Life was not easy for Europe, not easy for the nation, and (though not as earthshaking) not easy for me; but it would have been easier if, one night Mr. Pickering had not said:

"Kid, I think she's time I said good-by."

"You've *enlisted?*" I said. Three on the first trick had.

"Don't be a bird," he said.

"But saying good-by . . ."

"It ain't me that's leaving. It's you."

"Me?"

"Well, here we are in July and I'm taking my vacation in August, and in September you'll be in college, singing boola boola, and . . ."

"Mr. Pickering, there's something I have to tell you. It . . ."

"You and that pretty little girl of yours has been nice to me, so I want to do something nice for the two of you. What I'm saying is . . ."

"When September comes, I'll still be . . ."

"That I want you and her to come to Coney Island, be my guests, I mean, and eat hot dogs and ride the merry-go-round, and that. We'll go up on the 'Island Queen.' I figure . . ."

"Mr. Pickering, I'm not going anywhere. When September comes, I'll still be . . ."

157

"That next Wednesday would be nice. We're both off. How does next Wednesday sound to you?"

"But . . ."

"Oh, and I've invited Duveneck. If I know him, he'll be the only bird on the boat that's wearing water wings."

And that was that.

Kathleen was impressed, but she remembered the dinner party at Izzy Kadetz's.

"Will Mrs. Bruce be there, too?" she said.

"No," I said. "She won't touch Mr. Pickering with a ten-foot pole."

"But is he over her?"

"I guess he'll never be," I said. "But he's not as bad as he was. If he was, there wouldn't be a roundhouse left."

We were sitting on her front porch and the afternoon was warm.

"I think it's sweet of him to invite us," she said, but her voice was grave.

"Then why aren't you happy?" I said.

She gave the swing a push and didn't answer. She didn't have to; I knew. August was zooming at us fast and September was staring down our throats. September, Kathleen would start to college. She had catalogs around the house and her mother had started planning her wardrobe. For her life was busy, still going on; for me—well, no use getting maudlin.

I tried to cheer her.

"By September," I said, "we'll probably be at war, or the draft will get me. Maybe I should enlist. My mother could live on the allotment. Two of the apprentices enlisted last week. They . . ."

"Oh, George!"

She was frowning at me. I hadn't cheered her much. She was afraid.

"When they want you," she said, her voice stubborn, "they'll find you. Let's not talk about it."

It wasn't the easiest summer for the world, or us.

158

"George?"

"Yes?"

"I'm scared," she said simply. "Of September, of everything . . ."

You can see that other outings had happier beginnings. Ours started out hip-deep in gloom: mine, Kathleen's, Mr. Pickering's, and Mr. Duveneck's.

The day before the holiday, Mr. Duveneck confessed that he had tried to enlist in the army, navy, marines, coast guard, and—even though they weren't taking enlistments— the Secret Service and the FBI. He had been turned down by all of them: flat feet, high blood pressure, a terrible sinus condition, a bad heart, and—which came as a surprise—color blindness. "They said I had nice teeth, though," he told us, trying to salvage something.

With a blast of its whistle, the "Island Queen" got under way. The four of us stood up front on her fourth deck to watch the side-wheeler head upstream.

"Of course," said Mr. Duveneck, "what does the military know? They didn't ask me about push-ups, and I can do more push-ups than that marine recruiting sergeant. You should have seen his face. Nothing like the faces they got on their posters. His face didn't even have muscle tone. What kind of marine corps they got these days?"

"Don't take her so hard," said Mr. Pickering.

"It ain't me that's shortchanged," the hostler said. "It's America. I'm going to write to Charles Atlas about it."

He studied the river and his eyes were sad.

Kathleen looked at him out of the corner of her eyes.

"He looks pretty low," she murmured so only I could hear. "I hope he doesn't jump overboard and end it all."

"He wouldn't do that," I said to her. "He can't stand water in his nose."

"Brother!" she grinned.

The river breeze blew her hair and made her more beautiful than a girl has a right to get.

If you were a bird you'd fly a five and a half mile straight

line between downtown Cincinnati and Coney Island, but
the "Island Queen" wasn't a bird: she was a floating palace
painted white and green. She could carry four thousand passengers, had seven thousand lights, a ballroom with twenty
thousand square feet of hardwood dance floor, and thirty-
six watertight compartments, and was, they say, unsinkable.
The all-steel lady was a glittering side-wheeler that burned
oil but had a steam calliope. She was a five-deck creature
who couldn't fly a straight line: the river she followed took
ten miles to cover the same distance a bird could cover in
five and a half.

Once clear of the wharf, the "Island Queen"—smoke blowing from her high twin stacks, pennants whipping in the
river wind, and her calliope playing "Happy Days Are Here
Again"—pushed upstream. First she went southeast, past the
mouth of the Licking River, and ducked under the Central
Bridge that carried cars and trolleys to Kentucky. Beyond
the bridge, she turned northeast and went under the L&N
Railroad bridge. A few miles later—the Dayton sandbar and
the Eastern Avenue pumping station behind her—the "Island
Queen" swung south. A mile and a half after the Little Miami River empties into the Ohio, the "Island Queen" tooted
her whistle and there she was—at Coney Island!

But there was more to the trip than a half-hour ride on a
pretty boat. The view was one continuous spectacle. In that
ten mile run, the history of the valley had been compressed.
It is an open-air museum and a gigantic recollection. On
the Ohio side, most of the way you see Cincinnati: past,
present, and suggestions of the future; factories belching
smoke; shantyboats clustered beneath bridge piers; yacht
clubs with speedboats and sailboats; the cumbersome Rube
Goldberg machinery of river terminals; kids catfishing from
johnboats; and, always, the craggy spectacular of Mount
Adams high above you with its toy people watching you
from the toy windows of their toy tenements that dangle
from the slope. You pass the remnants of riverboats that
have no stern wheels and no stacks, that are rusted and

160

warped hulks robbed of identity, rotting, and remembered only by the river's wash. On the Kentucky side, beyond the Dayton sandbar, a different world appears: the Ohio Valley of long ago, a wild and lonely country that only the Indians knew. Now and then, breaking the mood, is a farmhouse, but mostly there's only trees. Here and there quick little beaches appear and swimmers, lazing in the sun, watch your boat go by. And, if you have sharp eyes, sometimes among the trees you might see a couple swimming nude. They usually hid, though, when the "Island Queen" appeared. The "Island Queen" had too many eyes.

The cost of the ride, which included admission to Coney Island itself, was thirty-five cents for adults; for children, two dimes. Four times a day, Tuesday through Friday, the "Island Queen" went upstream to Coney Island. It's first trip was at eleven in the morning and its last at eight at night. On Saturdays, Sundays, and holidays, it made an extra trip each way. The park was closed on Mondays. The last trip from Coney Island to Cincinnati departed at 10:45 weekdays and 11:30 P.M. on Saturdays, Sundays, and holidays. If you missed the last boat from the park, you could always catch a bus, but what fun was that? The real fun was coming back on the "Island Queen" when the night was mellow and the breeze was cool. If the Coney Island people had kept count, which would have been impossible, I'll bet they would have found that two out of every five Cincinnati marriages had begun on the "Island Queen's" top deck, romantically called the Moon Deck, especially when it wasn't raining and when the moon was powerful. I knew there was always kissing going on up there. But when I was a child, my mother would never let me go up and watch.

Throughout most of the trip upstream Mr. Pickering stood in front of the calliope and stared. He stared at the calliope. He stared at the steam it made. He stared at the man who played it. And when the musician took a break to stroll around the deck, Mr. Pickering didn't. He ignored the passing scenery and the way the girls' skirts were blowing;

he stared at the calliope. When the musician returned, Mr. Pickering stared at him. The musician blushed, played, hid his face behind clouds of steam, but whenever the steam parted, he saw Mr. Pickering staring. Maybe that was why the musician hit some sour notes that trip. Usually his calliope playing was perfect.

Mr. Duveneck at first leaned over the rail beside Kathleen and me but soon began to pace the deck—round and round and round. Children were everywhere, so were their parents; all were filled with good will, their good will was contagious, but Mr. Duveneck was immune. He paced round and round, growing whiter each time I saw him, and he seemed worried about something.

Kathleen, beside me, squinted against the sun's glare on the water, and was at peace. The river does that sometimes. It was as if she had left all sadness back on Cincinnati's public landing.

"I love the river," she said. "Don't you?"

"Yes," I said, "but she's a fooler."

"*She?*"

"I always thought of the river as a 'she,'" I said. "I guess that's dumb, though."

Kathleen studied the river thoughtfully.

"Is she nice?"

"It depends," I said. "Every day she's different."

"Mmmm," said Kathleen—and retreated somewhere inside herself I couldn't reach.

Maybe she was thinking about the river. I know I was.

My trouble is, I'm not *sure* of her—the river, I mean. No one who lives around her is. Mostly she's a lady and in back of our house she heads west. But the wind blows east and if you don't know the river well, you'd swear the way her ripples run upstream against the current that she was heading east, too. There's no telling about her. Sometimes she has ripples and sometimes white caps. Sometimes she's blue. Sometimes she's green. Sometimes she's brown with bottom mud. And sometimes she looks the way old woodcuts do: misty, far off, and unreal.

They say she has fish in her, but the one fish I caught was a tiny catfish that smelled of oil the way, upstream, the Beaver Valley in Pennsylvania smells (as if they took the whole valley—trees, houses, people, and all—and dipped it into oil for flavoring). Men in houseboats set trotlines on her; I'm not sure what they catch; they never say, because trotlines are illegal. In 1924, they say, a man at Foster, Kentucky, caught a channel cat that weighed twenty-eight pounds and was three feet long. His name was L. C. Stanley, in case you want to look it up. But if the Ohio River does have fish in her—catfish, northern pike, bream, black bass, and crappie—you can't prove it by me. I only caught that one and never went fishing again.

She doesn't *smell* of fish, though. Mostly she smells of river stink and oil. They say rivers purify themselves every ten miles. Perhaps. Between Dam 36 at New Richmond and Dam 37 at Fernbank, the Ohio River flows more than a dozen miles, sewers empty into her, creeks dump waste, three streams pollute her, and she has no chance to clean herself up at all. So rules of thumb don't work with her.

I like her most because she's wet with history. George Washington floated down her. John Audubon studied her birds. Andrew Jackson went east on her to be president. President Harrison's body went west on her to be buried. Washington Irving got caught in a drizzle on her, Charles Dickens wrote about her, Stephen Foster sang songs about her, Mark Twain made jokes about her, and slaves sneaked across her. Remember *Uncle Tom's Cabin* and Eliza crossing the ice? That was the Ohio River. People have drowned in her, steamboats have blown up on her, bridges have spanned her, and a lot of boats have worked her: the "Guiding Star," "Queen City," "General Crowder," "Omar," "Betsy Ann," "Cincinnati," and all the boats the Greene Line ran. She floods. Her worst was in '37. She freezes over. In '40 she froze solid for thirty days. In, on, and around her, they

163

put up government lights, daymarks, and buoys, but she doesn't care. They dredge her bottom for a channel; she wiggles and they have more mud than they can shake a stick at. They put up fifty dams to corset her, but she pays no attention. What I'm saying is, she's got a mind of her own. She flows along so sweet, but she sends boats to the boneyard and they rot while she stays good as new.

So much for the Ohio River.

By the time the "Island Queen" was putting in at the Coney Island dock, the decks were deserted because everyone crowded at the swinging stage, wanting to be off for first crack at the Coney Island rides. The calliope player, by this time unsure of anything, stopped playing and, filled with gloom, walked away. Mr. Pickering came to where Kathleen and I stood: still leaning on the fourth-deck rail and watching the people below. Through the trees and above them we could see the spidery high-rise structures of the park: mostly the roller coaster called the Wildcat with its dips, turns, climbs, and hair-raising cars.

"Well, here we is," said Mr. Pickering. "Now, remember. The day is on me. She's going to be my treat. The first thing we got to get you kids is a hot dog. All kids like . . ."

"Mr. Pickering," I said. "That's nice, but it's early. I'm not hungry and . . ."

He hadn't heard a word I said. ". . . hot dogs. Then we'll win your girl a Kewpie doll because what's the use of Coney Island if nobody wins a Kewpie doll? Then maybe we'll ride the shoot-the-chutes." He looked at the roller coaster, troubled. "I keep forgetting how high she is," he said. "Anyway, we'll ride the Ferris wheel." He saw that peeping over the treetops, too. "Say, she's up there, ain't she?" He looked sad. He was wondering what he had let himself in for. "Why don't we stick to hot dogs?" he said, wishing he were dead.

Mr. Duveneck arrived.

"Well, are we going to stand here all day?" he said. "I don't hold much to boats anyway. She was really pitching coming up the river, wasn't she?"

164

The "Island Queen" was too heavy to pitch but we didn't tell Mr. Duveneck. His face was white.

"All I know," he said, "is that I don't feel so good."

"What you need," said Mr. Pickering, "is a hot dog. It's good for what ails you."

Mr. Duveneck's face got whiter.

"Come on, you guys," said Mr. Pickering, his invitation including Kathleen. "They is getting to the hot dog stand ahead of us. We better get going."

We went down to the first deck. Mr. Duveneck walked as if he were walking on eggshells.

"They oughtn't to run a little boat like this when the river is acting up," he said. "Suppose she sank? I should have brought my water wings. A man can't be too careful . . ."

But once on land, Mr. Duveneck felt better. He gulped air, rubbed his stomach, and stopped walking the way he had been.

"She's always good to get ashore," he said. "If God had wanted man to be in the water, He would have given us gills. I feel the same about flying. If God had wanted man to . . ."

"Come on," said Mr. Pickering. "We'll get some hot dogs."

"If God," said Mr. Duveneck, "had wanted man to have hot dogs, He would have put a hot dog stand in the Garden of Eden."

"I never looked at it that way," said Kathleen. She was getting the biggest kick out of Mr. Duveneck but, always the lady, she hid it. I could tell, though.

We walked through the picnic grove between the landing and the park itself. Already a few families, with the determination of settlers, had staked claim to their picnic tables, plunked down their picnic hampers, and—with stony eyes and arms folded—prepared to do damage to any claim jumper who might appear. They gave us dark looks as we passed and seemed relieved once we were beyond them; their relief lasted until others came along behind us. They had come to Coney Island to enjoy themselves and they meant to do it even if they had to call a cop or belt someone.

"The hot dog stand is over . . ." Mr. Pickering said, leading the way, but when he stopped in his tracks, we did the same: we stopped and stared where he was staring.

Staring back at us, cotton candy in each fist, was Mrs. Bruce.

And at her side, in her shadow, dwarfed by her size, but looking smug, was a B&O brakeman who weighed ninety pounds.

21

Coney Island is a collection of sounds, scents, and sights. The sounds, then, were varied: the noise that families make and the barker's cry to guess your weight; the scratchy music of the merry-go-round, the screams of passengers as the roller coaster plunged, and the compressed-air hiss that blew a lady's skirt waist high, plus her cry of wonder and rage; the babble of picnickers, the squawk of a penny-arcade noisemaker, and the Dodg'em's crashes and smashes. The scents, then, were also varied: popcorn, perfume, mustard, and the swimming pool's chlorine; root beer, cotton candy, and the sweat of children. The sights, then, were just as varied: people dressed too casually, too brightly, or too formally; the frightened faces of the roller-coaster riders; the calculating eyes of the man at the ringtoss game; fat men in shirt sleeves drinking paper cups of beer; grand-mothers cooling in the shade; leggy girls who preened them-selves before the swimming pool's male gallery; half-pints blackmailing parents into "one more ride!"; and Kathleen, serene and cool and beautiful, walking along under a sun that smothered the rest of us. Coney Island was—and is—a passionate oasis from the ordinary, where for a few coins a man, momentarily, might experience ecstasy. But the wild-est sight and the wildest sound *that* day was Mrs. Bruce.

Mrs. Bruce had not been anticipated by history. Coney Island had begun as a picnic grove operated by James

Parker, and until 1886, when new management took over, Coney Island was a gentle place. They named it Ohio Grove—and called it "The Coney Island of the West." An early Ohio Grove official, unaware of Mrs. Bruce's approach, said, "We intend that everything shall be first class. All ladies and children will be safe here as at home. We are determined to protect them and all bad characters will be made to keep straight or be excluded." Thus, at Coney Island Mrs. Bruce was protected from the men, but what the early officials hadn't considered was, who would protect the men from Mrs. Bruce?

"Beershot!" Mrs. Bruce called. "This freak—" she devastated the B&O brakeman with a glance "—ain't gutsy enough to ride the Dodg'em with me!"

"Uh . . . uh . . ." said Mr. Pickering. He didn't know what to do. Should he go to her? Or should he stay with us?

"Go ride the Dodg'em with her," I said. "We'll meet you at Lost River."

"But I invited you to . . ."

"Go ahead, Mr. Pickering," Kathleen said. "It's all right."

"Are you coming or ain't you?" Mrs. Bruce brayed, and wiped her sticky fingers on her middy front. Her middy? Well, she was dressed for a holiday. She wore a white—it *had* been white once—middy that, on her, looked like a mainsail; a vast navy-blue skirt that had, somehow, gotten twisted—its side was in front and it was hanging wrong; a sailor hat that said *Souvenir of Chester Park*; dirty anklets; and high heels. She was a nautical nightmare.

Wading into two more cotton candies—one in each hand—she waddled off to the Dodg'em; Mr. Pickering and the B&O brakeman, ignoring one another, trotted after her.

"I gotta see this," Mr. Duveneck said. "I don't think they got a Dodg'em car her size."

Kathleen and I didn't attend. We walked slowly through the park to Lost River to wait for Mr. Pickering.

He wasn't long in coming.

He was distressed.

Mr. Duveneck was grinning.

"I *knew* they didn't have a car her size," the hostler said. "Them cars is designed for people, not crowds."

Mr. Pickering, blushing, tried to change the subject.

"Did you kids want to ride a boat through Lost River?" he said. "She's dark in there and people smooch. Maybe we'd better try the merry-go-round and . . ."

"Let's all go in Lost River," I said.

"In a boat?" cried Mr. Duveneck. "Kid, you know how I feel about boats. They . . ."

"You can always step out on land if the going gets rough," I said.

"Please, Mr. Duveneck," Kathleen said.

"I don't mean to be a spoilsport, but . . ."

"Here we is," said Mr. Pickering, who had drifted away during the conversation. "I got four tickets. Let's go."

Paling, Mr. Duveneck consented.

We went to the loading ramp where the boats were stopped for passengers and all climbed into one boat. Kathleen and I, at Mr. Pickering's direction, took the front seat. "So's I can keep an eye on you in case she sinks," Mr. Pickering said. "Sinks?" cried Mr. Duveneck, who, having sat beside Mr. Pickering, began to scramble back out. "Just an expression," said Mr. Pickering as he pulled the hostler back into the boat. "I may hold my breath the entire trip," said the hostler. He sounded as if he meant it.

Just as the attendant was going to release the brake that sent our boat on its way, I felt the boat jar, I felt it settle deeper, and I saw that the water level in the canal had risen. I turned to see what happened.

Sitting behind Mr. Duveneck and Mr. Pickering, occupying a full seat herself, sat Mrs. Bruce, a cotton candy in each hand.

"Boat rides is swell," she sneered. "Shove her off!" she commanded the attendant.

He released the brake and away we went.

169

The B&O brakeman, left behind, stared with gloom at the departing boat.

"I wouldn't let him come," she announced. "Boat rides make him horny."

The rest of us shuddered—and pretended she wasn't there.

Lost River is a lovers' ride with adventure at its conclusion. Little boats, moved by the current that Coney Island manufactures, travel in a narrow canal—one boat wide—into a shed that's black as pitch. There is only darkness, the boat scraping, water lapping, and—upon occasion—the complaint of an unseen girl in an unseen boat, "Do that again and you'll have no teeth." The boat travels a great distance but it doesn't get far; it weaves back and forth until you arrive at daylight and the exit ahead.

"I forgot *this* part," said Mr. Pickering.

He didn't care for adventure.

"This part is fun," I said.

"Mr. Duveneck," said Kathleen, "are you all right?"

He said nothing.

I looked back. In the glimmering daylight I saw he was white as a sheet. And he had his hands over his eyes.

"It'll be all right," I said.

He refused to be consoled.

"I can't talk now," he gasped. "I'm holding my breath."

In the seat behind them Mrs. Bruce sat as she had during the entire trip: her eyes not on the adventure but on the cotton candy in her hand. She had not come for adventure. She had come to eat.

Once out of the dark shed and into the daylight, we blinked and heard the ratchet noise and the waterfall noises that combined to introduce the adventure. The boat, pushed by the current, eased into an inclined plane. Continuous clogs in the incline grabbed the boat, hoisted it out of the water, and dripping wet, slowly up; Coney Island fell away below us. At the top of the incline there would be a pause, the boat would teeter, tilt, and zooooooom! hurl

170

down the other side a mile a minute, and at the last moment, the ramp would level off a little to shoot the boat and its squealing passengers into the pond and across it. Having survived another adventure the boat would drift back to the starting place and, ordinarily, that would be that. In our case, though, that *wasn't* that.

First, consider our trip up the incline. Usually the boats went up slowly, but ours climbed even slower. The man who worked the machinery that started the boats up the ramp looked troubled.

"Can't you make this thing climb faster?" Mrs. Bruce shouted at him. She shouted other things, too.

"Lady," he shouted back, "you should have gotten the next boat. This incline can only lift so much. It . . ."

As we got higher, his voice got lost in the noise of the ratchets and the waterfall, but what he said made an impression on me. What would happen when we slithered pell-mell down the other side and into the water? Would the boat float back to its starting place? Or, was there too much ballast? Would it hit the water, sink to the bottom, and drown us all? Also, there was a problem that was more pressing: was the ratchet device that hauled us up the ramp strong enough? Suppose it broke under the strain and instead of climbing up, we zoomed down backward, hurled the wrong way back into Lost River, crashing into oncoming boats head on?

"It'll be all right," I said to Kathleen.

She didn't say a word. She hadn't found comfort in my comment and, for that matter, neither had I.

"Beershot!"

Mrs. Bruce was shouting at Mr. Pickering.

"Uh . . . uh . . ."

The boat, at least, had reached the top and was teetering.

"After this here ride, I want to ride the Ferris wheel," she said. Her weight hindered the boat's teeter. It couldn't *quite* tip over to glide down the plane. I felt panic. Mrs. Bruce felt nothing. ". . . That B&O brakeman is scared

171

silly of Ferris wheels . . ." Teeter, teeter. ". . . so you got to take me for a ride on one. That's not the kind of ride that . . ." Finally the boat was tilting. ". . . a lady goes on alone. And I need . . ." Zoooooom! Down the ramp! Would we sink? Would we survive? ". . . some more cotton candy. Buy me some cotton . . ." *SPLASH!* Overloaded—and wobbling crazily—the boat almost upset but managed to right itself at the last moment; we had survived and were drifted to the loading platform. ". . . candy the minute we get off this stupid thing! You hear me? I want cotton candy!"

"Yes, Rosalind, yes," said Mr. Pickering as we all got out of the boat. "But first, I promised these kids . . ."

"COTTON CANDY!"

"Yes, Rosalind . . ."

He trailed after her to the cotton-candy concession and the B&O brakeman hustled after them both.

Kathleen and I would have followed, but the attendant at Lost River grabbed my arm.

"Buddy," he said, "you better do something about that." He pointed.

Mr. Duveneck, hands still over his face and still holding his breath, sat frozen in the boat.

"Mr. Duveneck," I said.

He didn't hear me.

I tapped him on the shoulder.

"The ride is over," I said.

He didn't budge.

"Buddy," said the attendant, "you're tying up my boats. Gimme a ticket and you can ride again if . . ."

Ride again? Never!

Mr. Duveneck was a streak exiting from the boat.

But he didn't talk for the longest time. He walked on the other side of Kathleen as we moved to the Ferris wheel. He had, though, taken his hands from his face and I was pleased to see that he had stopped holding his breath.

I didn't have too much time to consider him. The sight of Mr. Pickering attracted my attention. He was in a Ferris

172

wheel car, Mrs. Bruce was beside him, and the Ferris wheel had stopped with them at the top while its operator, his face worried, tried to figure out a counterbalancing device without putting ten people into one car. Mr. Pickering, afraid of heights and everything else, had shut his eyes. His grip on the bar in front of him, I could tell, was a death grip. Mrs. Bruce paid no attention to where they were. She was stuffing cotton candy into her mouth. She didn't care for the view. She could have seen the river from up there, all of Coney Island, the racetrack, and the country-side beyond. She saw none of these things. All she saw was cotton candy, disappearing fast.

"Let's walk by the lake," Kathleen said. There was no reason for us to stay and watch Mrs. Bruce. Everyone else in the park was doing that. We pretended, as we moved to the lake, that we didn't hear the comments of the crowd: "Did you ever see one that fat before?" . . . "See what happens when you eat between meals!" . . . and . . . "Frankly, she must be an ad for something, but God knows what!"

It was nicer by the lake. The sounds of the park were muted and shade trees were everywhere. Kathleen and I rented a canoe, paddled to the far side where more stillness was, and drifted.

She seemed pensive.

"This hasn't been too nice a day, has it?" I said.

She watched a swan glide by.

"It hasn't been too nice a summer," she said.

Other couples in other canoes paddled along; they were all happier than us. I could tell by the way they joked and the way they laughed.

Kathleen looked at me and I saw pain in her eyes.

"I'll never be able to say good-by to you," she said.

"There's Mr. Pickering at the pier," I said. "We better go."

Talking wasn't helping us.

"All right," she said.

173

We didn't speak as I paddled back across the lake. But as we neared the pier I had to say it.

"Kathleen?"

"Yes?"

I let the canoe drift.

"I love you. You know that, don't you?"

"But what is the good of knowing it?" she said simply. "We were going to love each other forever."

There was no need to say more; forever had dropped dead on us.

Nor did we have time for melancholy. Mrs. Bruce had seen Mr. Pickering at the canoe rental. As we docked, she was by his side, stuffing herself with more cotton candy, and whining:

"Rent me a pink canoe! Guys on the B&O has no imaginations. They don't know what ladies like. Ladies like canoe rides!"

Mr. Pickering, still undone by the Ferris wheel adventure, said:

"Uh . . . uh . . ."

Everyone was gaping at the size of Mrs. Bruce. Little children, seeing her, were so impressed that some let go of their balloons, which drifted to Fort Thomas, Kentucky. The children never noticed their departure. They were staring at Mrs. Bruce. They thought she was an attraction created for their amusement.

The B&O brakeman, crushed by Mrs. Bruce's remarks, was studying his fingernails, pretending what was happening, wasn't.

"Come on!" Mrs. Bruce sneered.

Several questions presented themselves to those in attendance. Would Mrs. Bruce *fit* into a canoe? And, if she would, what about the theory of water displacement? Would she cause the artificial lake to overflow? Would she, perhaps, flood the park itself via a tidal wave, unsettle the swans, wash away the Ferris wheel, and create panic among the picnickers?

174

These questions, also, plagued the man who rented the canoes. He tried to be diplomatic.

"Lady," he said, "all the canoes are rented. I got no canoe for you."

She would have none of that.

"I want a pink one!" she said.

As you know, she added other comments.

The canoe rental man shuddered.

"Watch your mouth," he said. "There are others around."

"PINK CANOE!" she bellowed.

Mr. Pickering couldn't look into the man's eyes. He looked, instead, at the man's shoe tops and mumbled:

"Please. I'd like to rent a pink canoe."

"For *her?*"

"Uh . . . you might say that."

"And *you're* going out with her in it?"

"Please. I'd like to rent a pink canoe."

"Mac, we don't have no Coast Guard here. Suppose you get out there and sink? I got no way of . . ."

"How about a blue one?"

"That's not the point, Mac."

"But . . ."

It was too late. While Mr. Pickering was discussing the situation with the man, Mrs. Bruce walked along the wooden pier, caused it to creak, and without a word, stepped down into a pink canoe, almost swamping it, but not quite. It wobbled, tilted, settled up to its gunnels in water, but it didn't sink, the lake didn't flood, and—by adjusting her fat—she managed to acquire the canoe around her waist. It was good that she sat in the middle. Had she sat in one end, the other would have tipped out of the water, her end would have gone under, and—well, you've seen newsreels of sea disasters.

"Beershot!" she shouted. "Come on!"

Mr. Pickering carefully got in, picked up a paddle, and with the look of a man who has just discovered he had gone through the day with his fly open, eased the canoe away from the pier.

"To the other side of the lake," Mrs. Bruce bawled. "I think I see some swans doing it!"

"I think," said Mr. Duveneck, who had witnessed the entire scene, "I'll go fish in the fishpond."

"Yes," said Kathleen. "George, let's take a walk. There's no need for us to wait here and . . ."

What they were saying was: let's scram before loudmouth does it again.

"Can Beershot swim?" said Mr. Duveneck as we walked away. "It's something I never thought to ask him. In the roundhouse, there was no need."

"The lake isn't *that* deep," I said.

"With her on it," he said, "it's deeper than you think."

We left him at the fishpond and took a walk.

I have neither the heart nor the adjectives to describe all the events of that day. Mrs. Bruce never let Mr. Pickering alone—and she never ditched the B&O brakeman, either. She used Mr. Pickering's money for rides and the brakeman's money for cotton candy. By twilight the front of her middy where she wiped her hands was sticky with pink cotton-candy smears.

Mr. Duveneck, seeing the way things were developing, spent the rest of the day at the fishpond, where he won six king-size buttons that said KISS ME QUICK, CHICKEN INSPECTOR, I LOVE MY WIFE BUT OH YOU KID, GARTER INSPECTOR, CATCH ME IF YOU CAN, SOUVENIR OF CONEY ISLAND, and SEE SEVEN STATES FROM ROCK CITY; an assortment of ashtrays; a gas-filled balloon; three miniature pocketknives; a ring marked *genuine imitation diamond;* two cigarette holders; and a harmonica worth ten cents retail.

Mrs. Bruce and Mr. Pickering rode on, among other devices, the merry-go-round (she wanted to ride a swan; there was none; she rode a green horse and sulked); the Wildcat (its operator wouldn't let anyone but Mr. Pickering on the

176

roller-coaster car with her; it held eight, but he said something about weight limits; Mrs. Bruce said something about his ancestors; and for a while, it was touch and go); and the Laugh-in-the-Dark, a little car that hustles you from one spooky scene to another while imitation cobwebs brush your face (but as the car wheeled around one sharp turn, Mrs. Bruce dropped her cotton candy, didn't laugh once, and threatened to bust the attendant's nose).

When night came, it found us wondering what to do. "Maybe," said Mr. Pickering, "I should ask Rosalind if she wants to ride back on the 'Island Queen' with us." He looked at her with hope. The B&O brakeman had purchased two more cotton candies for her, and she was berating him because a small child had gotten one that was bigger. The brakeman was looking the other way, pretending he didn't hear her, but his face was white, his hands trembled, and he had the hardest time putting his change back into his coin purse, which fastened with a snap. "She's been with *me* most of the day," said Mr. Pickering. "She wasn't with him."

"That's because he wouldn't ride the roller coaster," Mr. Duveneck said.

"Or the merry-go-round," Kathleen said.

"Or the Lost River or the Dodg'em, or the Ferris wheel. He wouldn't even take her canoeing."

Mr. Pickering shivered with recollection.

"Of course," he said, "you birds is my guests and it wouldn't be right to run out on you now to . . ."

"I'm not going back on the 'Island Queen' anyway," said Mr. Duveneck. "I'm going home on the bus." He gauged the sky. It was clear, mellow, and dripping with stars. "I think there's a storm brewing," he added.

"The wind ain't even blowing," said Mr. Pickering.

"Maybe," said the hostler, "that's because we're in the *eye* of the hurricane."

"What hurricane?" I said. "The weather has been . . ."

"Kid, you keep out of this," said Mr. Duveneck. "My

177

mind is made up. I'm going back on the bus. You'll never get me on that boat again!"

"But, Mr. Duveneck . . ."

"Kid, *you* can ride her all you want. That's because you're young and foolish. When you get to be my age, you'll practice caution. People my age is . . ."

"Older people than you ride the 'Island Queen,'" I said.

"I didn't say *their* age," he said. "I said *my* age. There's nobody *my* age that will ride the 'Island Queen.' Them others is older. Haven't you heard of senility?"

"But . . ."

"If he wants to go back by bus," said Mr. Pickering, "let him. She's a free country."

"Thanks," said Mr. Duveneck. "I was beginning to wonder."

He gave me a dirty look.

"What I'm saying is," said Mr. Pickering, "I can't leave you kids by yourselves. I done that too much today already."

"We can get home all right," I said.

"Come on the bus," said Mr. Duveneck. "She'll be safer."

"I'd like to go back on the boat," Kathleen said.

"You'll drown," said Mr. Duveneck. "Ain't you heard of the 'Titanic'? She struck this iceberg and . . ."

"It's August, Mr. Duveneck," I said. "There's no ice on the river. Besides, the 'Island Queen' has thirty-six watertight compartments. She's unsinkable."

"Yeah?" said the hostler. "Well, they said that about the 'Titanic,' too. Then along came this iceberg and—bloooie!"

"I'd still like to ride the boat back," said Kathleen.

"It's your funeral," said the hostler.

"What George and I are trying to say," Kathleen said to Mr. Pickering, "is that we've had a wonderful time. But we can all get back all right. Why don't you . . ."

Her voice trailed off and her glance indicated Mrs. Bruce. Mrs. Bruce, at that moment, had received two more cotton candies and was glaring in anger at the cotton candy a little girl had purchased. She discovered hers was bigger than the

178

child got and sneered happily at her victory; the B&O brakeman looked the other way, pretending he was invisible.

Mr. Pickering got tears in his eyes.

"You kids is so sweet," he said. "If it's really all right, I
mean, and it wouldn't put you out none . . ."

He was too overcome to speak.

He blew his nose with that great honking noise. The little
girl looked at him, pleased; she had never heard such beautiful music, so she waited for him to do it again, and was
disappointed when he didn't.

"I better get over and ask her," he said. "The way she's
been today has led me to believe . . . well, it would be
sweet, wouldn't it, if things worked out nice?"

He was suddenly shy.

"Go to her," Kathleen said gently.

"Now's your chance," I said. "Look."

The B&O brakeman, while Mrs. Bruce's back was
turned, was trying to sneak away.

"I guess it's now or never," said Mr. Pickering and stood
rooted, afraid to hope.

"Go on," I said.

Mrs. Bruce, out of cotton candy, was scanning the crowds
for the brakeman. She couldn't see him anywhere. He was
trying to infiltrate a family of ten, but the smaller children in
the group shoved him out every time he shoved himself
into the ensemble. The mother and father, exhausted by
the day's outing, attributed their clan's fighting to fussiness
on the part of the children, and I heard the father say,
"Settle down, all of you, and come along." But the children,
recognizing the B&O brakeman as an upstart, kept pushing
him; he kept pushing them, too, and a first class donnybrook
was building with screams, slaps, kicks, and shoves. The
father, fed up, waded in, restored order, and looked with
surprise and melancholy at the B&O brakeman. I could see
it in the father's eyes: he didn't approve of middle-aged
children. The brakeman, forsaken, sneaked away; and Mrs.
Bruce spotted him.

"COTTON CANDY!" she bellowed. "COTTON CANDY!"

Panic-stricken, the B&O brakeman began to run.

Mr. Pickering rushed in where B&O brakemen fear to tread. He hurried to the cotton-candy concession and said:

"Two cotton candies, please. And hurry."

The man behind the counter sighed.

"Can't do it, pal. My helper is going after more makings now. That fat slob ate me out of all of it. She . . ."

"COTTON CANDY!"

Mrs. Bruce's cry filled the park. Well, almost.

Mr. Pickering went to her.

"Rosalind," he pleaded, "there'll be more in a minute. The man ran out."

She put her fat hands where her fat hips should have been and, Mr. Pickering in her wake, waddled straight to the cotton-candy concession.

"What do you mean that you're out of cotton candy?" she bellowed. "Are you a Nazi or something?"

"Lady," said the man, "you can't talk that way about me. I was in the big war."

"*Which* side?" she brayed.

In anger, the man slammed his window shut, sat inside, and glared at her. His lips moved in silence. I didn't have to be a lip-reader to translate. He was saying, "Fat slob . . . fat slob . . . fat slob . . ."

"Beershot," she said, "they isn't out of beer. Gimme a paper cup of beer."

"Rosalind, you've had a lot of cotton candy. Will beer and cotton candy mix? Will . . ."

"BEER!"

In one hour Kathleen and I were on the boat, heading home. Somewhere, on land and in a bus, Mr. Duveneck was doing the same. The man from the cotton-candy concession was on the boat, staring with gloom at the water, and muttering, "Fat slob . . . fat slob . . ." The B&O brakeman was on the boat, too. He kept biting his nails and looking back upstream, as if Mrs. Bruce would come hustling on the water

180

after him. He seemed terribly upset. Shadows made him jumpy. Fat shadows made him jumpier.

Meanwhile, surrounded by a pile of paper cups that had once contained beer, Mrs. Bruce announced to Mr. Pickering that she always wanted to do it on the shoot-the-chutes.

"The poor little thing," Mr. Pickering told me later. "She passed out as soon as she climbed in the roller-coaster car. I guess that was just as well. But the men there couldn't lift her out. So they closed the shoot-the-chutes down for the night, covered her with tarpaulin to keep the dew off so she wouldn't catch her death of cold, and left her there all night to sleep it off. Ain't she sweet, though. She gets the biggest kick out of Coney Island. Maybe we'll spend our honeymoon there."

22

August was one long heat wave. I expected Mrs. Bruce to
cool off riding the turntable. She didn't and Mr. Pickering
seemed sadder. Each night he looked for her. "I mastered
that folding chair," he said. "It's a pistol." Kathleen was sad
that August, too, and so was I. The newspapers were filled
with college talk. Mr. Duveneck was sad that August. The
hostler read of the war in Europe and stared off into space.
He brooded because the military rejected him *carte blanche*
and wondered, on steamy nights, why Charles Atlas had
failed him.

One night I found Mr. Pickering in the locker room. He
was staring at a locomotive blueprint. Now and then, he
would make notes with a pencil stub. When he was aware
of me, he said:

"To beat the heat, she's a matter of keeping busy."

He looked vaguely about the room.

"I'll need some corn, though," he added.

"Corn?"

"Barley might do," he amended. "Maybe tomorrow I'll
stroll up Southside Avenue to that malt place Standard
Brands has got."

"Why?"

"Because I'll need malt, too," he said, yawned, and fell
asleep.

It was too hot to wake him up and ask him more.

I wondered about him, of course. The Standard Brands plant between the B&O tracks and Southside Avenue was a collection of beery, old red brick buildings that smelled of malt. They had been there for ages. Some said it was the largest malt-extract plant there was. Even the '37 flood that reached the second floor of the buildings couldn't wash away its heady aroma. Next door to it, in the carshop where special railroad tank cars were built and repaired to haul vinegar and acids, vinegar and acid smells mingled with the malt smell to make the neighborhood a symphony of discordant—and pungent—scents.

But the next night—the *last* night—when I came to work I saw that the buildings were still standing. I felt better.

I asked Mr. Pickering if he had been there.

"First things first," he said.

He went to his locker, got out the blueprints of the locomotive, spread the paper on the table, and stared at it vacantly.

"Are you studying to be a foreman?" I said.

"Don't be a bird," he said.

"Won't you give me a hint?" I said.

The heat was making me irritable—and so was he.

He digested this question.

"Well," he said, "look at her this way. There was a story in the Cincinnati *Post* last month about silk stockings. It said because of the shooting match in Europe, ladies would have to do without." He paused, looked puzzled, and added, "What do you suppose silk stockings has got to do with a war?"

"Was *that* your hint?"

He nodded and said:

"You mean you didn't catch on?"

"You could say that," I said.

He shoved the blueprints aside and concentrated on me.

"Well," he said, "look at her this way. What is them locomotives sitting out there?"

"Yard engines, passenger engines . . ."

"That's not what I meant, kid. They is boilers—on wheels. That's what they is."

"And?"

"They make steam," he said.

"And?"

"They need steam to make whiskey, don't they?"

I was afraid to ask the next question, but I had to.

"Mr. Pickering, are you thinking of making moonshine?"

He nodded.

"There is going to be all kind of shortages," he said. "If I was a lady, which as you know I ain't, I'd buy me some silkworms and make my own silk stockings. I hear they do it with spit."

"It's against the law to make moonshine!"

"It should be against the law," he said, "to make stockings with spit!"

I couldn't take any more of him. It was too hot. And he wasn't helping matters. I was exhausted. Sleep that day had been impossible. Kathleen and I had met, briefly, in town. Then she had to meet her mother to buy her college wardrobe. It wasn't the best meeting we'd ever had. So I left Mr. Pickering and went out to the turntable. I was like Greta Garbo. I wanted to be alone. But the night was piling up too fast.

As I dragged out to the turntable, I moved with my eyes half closed. The air was clammy, my overalls were clammy, and ice water hadn't made my thirst go away. A few feet from the turntable shanty I opened my eyes wider, so I wouldn't walk into the turntable pit, and I realized the turntable lights had been turned off. But they had been on thirty minutes before when I had gone into the roundhouse.

I went inside the control shanty and was about to light the lights again when, from the shadows, Mr. Duveneck whispered:

"Don't do that."

I turned on the lights.

"*That's* what I meant for you not to do," said Mr. Duveneck and turned them off.

"Mr. Duveneck," I said, "it's too hot. I don't feel like playing games. Besides, I can't work in the dark."

I turned the lights on.

"You'll have to learn to," he said.

He turned them off again.

"Why?" I said.

I left the lights off. I was too tired to argue.

"You don't see no lights on anywhere, do you?" he said. He pointed to the ashpit and the coal dock.

He was right. Usually the coal dock—a five-story Christmas tree loaded with coal and shaped funny—was aglow with lights everywhere; but that night all its lights were out. The string of lights at the ashpit were out, too, and so was the light in the Negro's shanty. The moonlight glistening on the rails was the only illumination.

"We're going to work this way from now on," said Mr. Duveneck.

"But the roundhouse has lights on," I said.

"I can't do anything about that," he said. "Out here is *my* responsibility."

"But why are you . . ."

"Ain't you read the papers?"

"Yes," I said, irritably. "But I miss a lot. Only tonight Mr. Pickering was telling me about making silk stockings from spit . . ."

"*I*," said Mr. Duveneck, peeved, "am talking about *fifth columnists!*"

"Around here?"

"Everywhere!" he said. "You heard how they done in Europe, didn't you? Sneaky. Dirty. That's what they is. King Arthur would never have approved. Anyway, there they is, and so we're making it hard for them."

I will not go on with the full conversation. It lasted hours. What Mr. Duveneck was doing was protecting the New York Central from a sneak attack. "Just the Indiana division," he said, "the rest is on their own; I'm only one man." He figured we were surrounded by fifth columnists. I tried to walk away, but he was holding my arm. I had to hear him out. He said they were hiding in bushes and peeping at us from behind trees. He said they were disguised as railroad men, old women carrying shopping bags, and streetcar motormen. He said when the right moment came they would throw off their disguises and, screaming rebel yells with a German accent, would storm the roundhouse and render it useless. He said having the lights off would make them stumble over tracks in the dark, fall down, and hurt themselves before they could hurt the railroad. He said a bunch of stuff.

"I thought of barbwire," he said, "but it costs too much and if Sourpuss Landsdowne got caught in it, there'd be no holding him."

Another item Mr. Duveneck tried to sell was his list of secret passwords.

"She's no longer a question," he said, hanging onto my arm, "of who is who because sometimes they is not who they is supposed to be. The Nazis might have someone who looks exactly like you, for instance, did you know that? Some night they might hit you over the head with a stick, throw your body in the river, and this guy who looked like you would take your place here, and who would be the wiser? That's why we need passwords."

"Mr. Duveneck, let go of my arm. I'm going in and get a drink of water and . . ."

"Here's the list of passwords. The password will change every ten minutes to confuse them if they're eavesdropping. The list is kind of long and complicated. So carry her with you all the time. Then, when we meet if you don't give the right password I'll know you're not you, but a Nazi, and I'll hit you in the neck with my Stillson wrench. Only I won't be hitting you. You'll already be dead; I'll be hitting the one I *thought* was you, but wasn't. The ashpit man we don't have to worry about. He's a Negro and the Nazis won't bring in a Negro to replace him. They're fed up with Negroes after what Jesse Owens did in the Olympics in Berlin. But they're clever, these Nazis. Only I'm trickier."

"Yes," I said, "but how do I know that you're you?"

"Huh?"

"Suppose you're a Nazi disguised as you?"

He drew himself up, outraged, but he didn't let go of my arm.

"How could I be a Nazi?" he demanded. "You *know* I'm me!"

"Yes, but who are you?"

"Kid, you're going about this wrong."

"Mr. Duveneck, if you're going to hit me with your Stillson wrench, don't I have the right to hit you with mine?"

And, believe me, right then I wanted to.

"No," he said. "If you give the right password, I won't hit you."

"But when the Nazis knock me out," I said, "won't they go through my pockets and get the password list? Then they'd give the right password, you wouldn't hit them, and there you are."

He looked crestfallen.

"Maybe we'll do without passwords," he said. "I'm a good judge of character. I can tell if you're a Nazi or not."

"How?"

"Have you watched the newsreels?" he said. "Nazis always wear Nazi armbands."

August was not only the cruelest month; it was the most exasperating month, too.

I tried my darndest to convince Mr. Duveneck that we'd better work with the lights on. If we didn't, I pointed out, we'd do more damage than the Nazi army, but he was hard to convince. "You're just a kid," was his response. But Mr. Richter, the third-trick foreman, wasn't a kid. When he came out to investigate the darkness, he said, "Quit horsing around, Duveneck, and get these lights on before somebody gets killed." After the foreman went back into the round-house, the hostler turned the lights on and muttered, "I'll

187

bet he's a fifth columnist. I've got to watch him like a hawk. The minute he forgets and wears his Nazi armband, I'm calling the FBI."

"Next," I said, "you'll be saying Mr. Pickering is a fifth columnist."

"He bears watching, too," said the hostler. "You watch him and I'll watch Richter."

"But . . ."

"Kid, I can't watch everybody! I'm only one guy. And Beershot *has* been acting peculiar. He's been studying locomotive blueprints like he was . . ." Mr. Duveneck stopped, frightened. "I'll bet that ain't Beershot at all. I'll bet he's a Nazi figuring how to sabotage . . ."

"Forget it, Mr. Duveneck," I said. "All he's trying to do is . . ."

I hesitated.

It was too hot for explanations.

Anyway, who would believe me?

"I'll keep an eye on him," I said. "You watch the foreman."

Mr. Duveneck was relieved.

"She's not easy defending a railroad," he said and walked up the track to the coal dock, studying each shadow as he went.

But can't you see the night was getting on my nerves? I sound as if I'm making excuses. I'm sorry. There is no excuse for the way I was with Mr. Pickering.

The last time I saw him alive was after lunch. Mr. Pickering—his blueprints within reach—was sitting in the opened front end of a dead locomotive in the deadhouse. Its front, like a can someone has opened, had been swung to the side on the great hinges. Inside, in the heat and rust and gloom of the smokebox, Mr. Pickering was examining the pipes that the water ran through. The water came from the tank via an injector, the pipes ran back and forth over the heat of the firebox, and eventually the water turned into steam and made the locomotive move.

188

I hadn't wanted to talk to Mr. Pickering. I had been looking for a quiet corner away from everyone where I could brood. I wasn't feeling my best what with the heat, the way the world was doing me, and all.

"Oh . . . kid . . ."

Not tonight, Mr. Pickering, I wanted to say. *Please, I can't stand any more of the world tonight.*

Only how was he to know?

"Come on up a minute, will you, and hold the light," he said. "It's simply a matter of rearranging this bird's plumbing and . . ."

I climbed up with him and sat with my feet dangling outside the smokebox.

"Mr. Pickering," I said, "why don't you lay off this idea? Now Mr. Duveneck thinks you're a Nazi in disguise, trying to sabotage the railroad."

"Duveneck is a bird," he said. "Hold the light over this way. Besides, kid, when I'm thinking about this, I'm not thinking about . . . well, you know."

But having mentioned it, he did think about it: his star-crossed romance with Mrs. Bruce.

He peered at me carefully.

He misread my frown.

"Don't be hard-nosed about her, kid," he said. His voice was lonesome. "Don't condemn what God ain't. Don't never do that."

If only it hadn't been so hot. The roundhouse where we were was so hot and so quiet it seemed to hum with silence. Now and then, breaking the silence, was the knocking noise the overhead steam line made; and then more silence and not a breath of air.

"It ain't that *I* ain't questioned things," he said. "I mean, is what we got, me and her, something wrong; or is she an angel that just got fat?"

"Let's not talk about it," I said. "What's the good of it?"

He was silent for the longest time.

"Kid," he said at last, "she's time we did have a talk."

189

"About Mrs. Bruce?"

"About you," he said. "Growing boys need man-to-man talks."

That did it!

"Mr. Pickering, I *know* where babies come from."

"Don't talk dirty," he said.

"It's not dirty. It's . . ."

"Watch your mouth," he said. I guess the heat—and the world—was chewing at us both. "It ain't easy doing man-to-man talks."

"Mr. Pickering, I *know* most . . ."

"Aw, come on now. Don't talk dirty."

I gave up, settled back, and refused to look at him. There was no escape.

"All right," I said irritably. "If you must, go ahead."

Sorry he had brought the matter up, he braced himself with a belt of Old Grand-Dad, but I must admit there was strength in him. He wasn't going to dodge the issue.

"Is we alone?" he asked.

"We're alone," I said.

He sat silent for a full minute, cleared his throat, and—in a different tone of voice—said:

"Life is like a roundhouse."

He waited an eternity for this thought to soak in. While waiting, he took another belt from his bottle.

"A roundhouse," he said, "is where men work hard and shoot the breeze. They make jokes about how women is. Some call their wives old ladies and brag how things is in bed . . ."

He took another drink for courage and plunged ahead.

"But I seen these same birds when they first come here young and sweet. They sit real quiet in corners kind of shocked by the talk that goes on. Only pretty soon they get married and where does the sweetness they got go? Because they is boasting like the rest and calling their wives old ladies, too . . ."

He stopped, distressed with remembering.

190

"Kid, every year there is new birds shocked by this talk and soon the shock wears off and they is the same as the rest. All the men here, me included, sat in corners one time that way, listening and pretending not to hear. But where is we now? We is yapping a mile a minute and turning our wives and girl friends into old ladies. Your old man was the same. I used to hear him brag . . ."

"*No!*"

"Kid, why should he be different? What makes you think you'll be different? Better birds than him and you has got caught up with what goes on. In five years, you'll be yapping like the rest."

"And *you*, Mr. Pickering?" I said, furious. "Are you any better?"

His strength wavered and was gone.

"No," he said. "I ain't and never was. But what does that mean? The only thing I'm saying is, you can't stay untouched forever. You ain't strong enough, kid. It ain't your fault. Nobody is. And them," he concluded sadly, "is the facts of life."

Well, I had some facts for him—and I gave them to him with both barrels.

"*This* is a fact of life," I said, hatefully. "I'm not going to college next month. I'm going to be right here. And it'll be the same next year, and the year after . . ."

He looked as if I had struck him.

"But you said . . ." he said. He couldn't go on.

"Some things," I said, my voice cold, "don't work out."

"No," he mumbled. "Some things has *got* to work out, or what's the good of anything!"

"Maybe *next* time," I said, fed up.

"But all the next times, kid, is now," he said.

He shook his head.

"I wished I'd saved the money I throwed away on drink," he said. "I'd hand her over to you . . ."

"Forget it," I said.

"No," he said. "Wait. I can borrow some. They got these friendly loan places. All you need is a name."

"No, Mr. Pickering, no!"

"But you can't let her go so easy," he said. "Here's what we'll do. I'll pay your rent. And buy the food. I'll . . ."

"Mr. Pickering, there *is* no way. Let me alone!"

"What about your pretty little girl? She . . ."

"A guy can't have everything," I said.

"But don't you *want* to go to college?"

Forgive me, but suddenly I was looking at him as Mrs. Bruce—and the rest of the world—looked at him: a bumbling, ineffectual old drunk who messed up everything he touched.

"I mean," he went on, "do you *want* to stay in the round-house?"

No! No! No!

"Kid, your old man said . . ."

"Beershot, shut up!"

I'm sorry. I'm shallow. But this old man was bothering me. Bothering? That's not the word. *I* was being destroyed. Not fast, but slowly, inch at a time, day at a time, until the years piled up and crushed me. I'm not trying to be dramatic about this: I'm trying to be honest. And, honestly, right then, I hated him. I had no pity for him. I needed every ounce of pity for myself. And that's why—*forgive me, forgive me*—I called him Beershot. I wanted to hurt him as the world had hurt me.

And I hurt him, I hurt him deep.

"Uh . . . uh . . ." he said. Don't talk to me about pain. You should have seen the pain I put in his eyes.

"Don't make a freak of me," I shouted at him. "Just because you're a freak doesn't mean the rest are freaks, too!"

He stumbled to his feet. I can't describe his eyes.

"Beershot?" he said. "But you always called me Mr. Pickering . . ."

"I had to come out of that corner sometime, didn't I?" I said.

"Uh . . . uh . . ." But the words would not come.

I sat trembling as he climbed out of the front of the engine and shuffled away. I tried to justify myself. He had insulted my father, hadn't he? And what was he trying to do to me? Who was he, anyway? Well, after he had gone, I settled down. I was ashamed. Tomorrow night, I told myself, Mr. Pickering and I would talk things over. Maybe it would rain and we'd feel better. Heat has a way of making things worse. Rain would be nice. We'd sit out where it was cool, we'd talk about all kinds of things, and I would tell him how sorry I was. He would be himself, again, and for us, things would be nice, the way they had been. Yeah. I'd do all these things the next night. It was too hot to run after him and say them then. There would be time next time. I was there forever. Mr. Pickering and I would have all the time in the world. But Mr. Pickering had said it best: "All the next times is now."

The next time was to be the next night—but the next night he was dead.

23

Three days after they found Mr. Pickering's body beside the tracks, I sat in the funeral parlor and heard the minister saying:

"... *Now is Christ risen from the dead, and become the firstfruits of them that slept. For since by man came death, by man also the resurrection of the dead. For as in Adam all die . . ."*

The parlor was stuffy. The electric fan that hummed over the door did no good. The air was so humid I could have sliced it with a knife. The rain, having stopped, was coming again. Under my coat, my shirt stuck to my back. It was sopping wet. Mr. Duveneck suffered the same way. So did Mr. Burkholder, the roundhouse general foreman; Mr. Richter, the third-trick foreman; and Mrs. Bruce, who could not adjust her fat to make the heat go away. Mr. Martin, the first-trick turntable operator, was too provoked to feel the heat. He made clicking noises with his false teeth, frowned at the coffin where Mr. Pickering's body was, and wondered why God had forgotten him to grab off a younger man instead. At her organ, her back to us, Kathleen sat: head bowed, hands folded in her lap, so strong, so beautiful. In his coffin, the center of attention, Mr. Pickering napped. But he wasn't napping, was he? He was dead.

"... *he shall have delivered up the kingdom to God, even*

194

the Father; when he shall have put down all rule and all authority and power . . ."

Only seven of us were there: the two foremen, Mr. Duveneck, Mr. Martin, Mrs. Bruce, Kathleen, and me. If we hadn't needed pallbearers, I wonder who would have attended at all.

Three dozen folding chairs, stenciled with the funeral home's advertising, lined the room: four rows of nine chairs each. The funeral director had hoped for a bigger attendance, but as at a movie no one cares to see, his funeral parlor was practically empty. While the minister said sing-song words of good-by to Mr. Pickering, the director stood in the back of the room, smiled the smile he was supposed to smile, inventoried the four displays of flowers and that one wreath the roundhouse sent, and calculated their worth. That done, to kill more time, he did sums in his head of other funerals, wished he had a frosty beer, and looked at his wristwatch. Funerals were old hat to him; he had seen them all.

But they were new to me. When my father died, my mother had handled things. There were no relatives to do the chore for Mr. Pickering. Somebody had to do it, so Mr. Duveneck and I took the job.

"Does he have a family burial plot?" the funeral director two days before had asked.

Mr. Duveneck and I didn't know and we had no way to find out.

"Oh," said the funeral director, who didn't know how to treat us. Should he express grief and murmur more? Or were we a disinterested committee? "What church did he attend?"

Mr. Duveneck looked at me and I looked at Mr. Duveneck. If we mentioned all the churches Mr. Pickering had tried, the funeral director would have kicked us out. As matters stood, they were confused enough.

For one thing, Mr. Pickering had no home. He had slept in fireboxes and he had stored his worldly possessions in his roundhouse locker, which, when opened, didn't yield much. It contained wads of dirty clothing, two fifths of Old Grand-Dad, a 1937 Cincinnati *Post* front page describing the 1937 flood, a ham sandwich that predated the newspaper, a Christmas card from the New York Central System, and a cigar box littered with odds and ends: combs, bolts, pieces of string, toothpicks, two bottle openers, three buttons, and twenty-nine cents in change. On him, when he died, had been his wallet. It had contained his union card, annual pass, a ticket stub from the burlesque house, and forty-seven dollars. That was his entire estate that we had discovered.

Have you ever tried to bury a friend for $47.29?

"Well," said Mr. Duveneck when we both got the assignment, "I guess I can toss in a hundred bucks. I was saving it to buy barbwire, but I can do without."

"And I've a hundred and ninety-seven dollars saved," I said. "I'll throw that in."

"Would Beershot have wanted you to, kid?"

"I was saving for something that cost too much," I said. "I've nothing else to use the money for."

"Okay," said Mr. Duveneck. "If that's the way you want it." His voice was gentle.

The pact was made. It was agreed that with $344.29 a friend could—after a fashion—be buried.

The funeral director unfolded a catalog.

"Here," he said, "are some very beautiful caskets. This one—" he pointed to a dandy "—is decorated with angel scrolls. All hand-tooled and . . ."

Mr. Duveneck had looked at its price, blushed, and said:

"We'd like to see something you got on sale. Or, maybe one you repossessed."

". . . *How are the dead raised up? and with what body do they come? Thou foolish one, that which thou sowest is not quickened, except it die . . .*"

To railroad men the actual funeral ceremonies are family affairs—and private. They said their good-bys the night before. Though it had been raining cats and dogs the night

196

before, they never stopped coming. They stood around the funeral parlor, dripped, and talked in hushes. The funeral parlor was packed with them. At times, the room got so crowded there wasn't enough air to breathe.

All the foremen showed up: the enginehouse foreman, the district boiler foreman, the drop-pit foreman, and the three gang foremen from the three tricks. The roundhouse office help came: the clerks, the engine dispatchers, and the call-boys, including Mr. Landsdowne. The blacksmith showed and so did the boiler inspector. Fourteen boilermakers appeared, three locomotive carpenters, five electricians, and six men from the rip track. The three federal engine inspectors dropped by. Forty of the forty-five machinists paid their last respects, so did eight pipe-fitters, eleven boilermaker helpers, four boiler washers, two dozen machinist helpers, three box packers, and the toolroom man. The roundhouse had twenty apprentices; nineteen were there and the twentieth was sick. Engineers and firemen came; switchmen, yard clerks, flagmen, conductors, and three one-armed crossing watchmen came, too. Strangers came: some were waitresses, some were bartenders, one looked like a fallen woman, two were newsboys who moved through the crowd and sold papers, and some were strangers—*complete* strangers—who came in because the funeral home was by a streetcar stop, it was pouring outside, and the streetcars ran fifteen minutes apart.

Mr. Pickering, as designed by the funeral home technicians, was the center of all attention.

"Don't he look good . . ."

"Say, they done a nice job on him . . ."

"He looks like he was sleeping . . ."

"I wonder how they make them look so natural . . ."

But now and then someone would be honest and say:

"That don't look like him at all."

"*. . . the resurrection of the dead. It is sown in corruption; it is raised in incorruption: it is sown in dishonor; it is*

197

raised in glory; it is sown in weakness, it is raised in power . . ."

Kathleen came in and straight to me. Drops of rain were on her face, she wore a black babushka, her hands were jammed deep into her raincoat pockets, and her raincoat glistened with wet. She stopped in front of me, beside the coffin, but she didn't once look at it; she looked at me.

"You look pale," she said.

"It's muggy in here," I said.

She nodded.

"It's nice outside," she said. "The rain cooled the streets. Let's take a walk."

"They need me here."

"I need you, too," she said.

Sloshing through the rain refreshed me. There was air to breathe. We didn't walk fast. There was no hurry. We walked as if there was no rain.

The funeral home wasn't in Sedamsville; it was downtown. I don't know why Mr. Duveneck and I picked it. We had been downtown that day to draw his hundred dollars from a building and loan association, had walked out Vine Street where Mr. Pickering used to roam, on a side street had been a funeral home, we had gone in, and that was that. The funeral, I suppose, should have been held in Sedamsville, but no one questioned why the services were held in a neighborhood of strangers.

That rainy night Kathleen and I walked the same streets Mr. Pickering had once walked. The neighborhood was poor. Two-story brick houses stood side by side, each front door opening onto the sidewalk. But the streets were wet and empty. Everyone was inside out of the rain. The rain rattled on the tin roofs, streamed down the brick walls, eddied across the sidewalk, cleansed the cobblestone street, and combined with the heat to make a mist rise. Three blocks ahead of us, through the rain and mist, we saw the lights of a streetcar crossing Sycamore. The streetcar's windows were fogged but passengers had rubbed circles to peer

198

out and see the night. Then, without a sound, the streetcar, seeking port, vanished; and Kathleen and I were alone.

She hadn't said a word. She was a pastorale—wet and wise—who knew better than to invent a happiness that wouldn't work. Plodding beside me, her arm tucked in mine, her head bent against the gusts, she matched my mood with absolute pitch. She was too honest to fence with me—and she was too sad.

We turned a corner, the rain came down harder, and we ran to the only shelter we could see: the marquee of a movie house they had condemned. The marquee extended over the sidewalk and offered sanctuary. The front of the theater itself had been boarded shut with plywood on which children had scribbled dirty words. On the marquee was the message:

WATCH FOR REOPENING SOON

but the message had been there too long. The people no longer waited. They had all gone away.

"George?"

Kathleen's face was a shadow; I could only see its outline. "Yes?"

"Everything is over, isn't it?"

"This isn't the time to talk about it," I said.

I could see how firm her jaw was. She could be obstinate at times.

"Will there ever be time to talk about it?" she said.

"I got so much on my mind right now," I said.

"Are you going to register next month?"

I watched a wet cat scoot across the street. I thought of Mr. Pickering. *All the next times is now.* The answer I gave Kathleen surprised me more than it did her.

"Yes," I said.

I didn't know how things were going to work. I only knew they had to work. I was running out of *next times*. I realized I'd probably starve. Not only me, but my mother would starve, too. We wouldn't be able to pay the rent. Our

199

furniture would be set out on the street. But I can't explain this. Suddenly, I realized none of these things would happen. Somehow or other, things would work out. They had to, didn't they? Or, as Mr. Pickering said, what was the use of anything?

A car drove by; its headlights lighted Kathleen's face, and I could see raindrops on her cheeks? Or were they tears? All I know is, she was smiling at me.

"... *As is the earth, such are they also that are earthy; and as is the heavenly, such are they also that are heavenly. And as we have borne the image of the earthy, we shall also bear the image of the heavenly* . . ."

When Kathleen and I returned to the funeral home I thought things there would be over, but I was wrong. There, drunk and disheveled, Mrs. Bruce stood. Her eyes were gritty with hate. Her fat lips were curved into a sneer. Water dribbled from her everywhere. She stood over the coffin, her hands on her hips, and gaped with disgust at the Mr. Pickering the funeral people had created.

"I seen Kewpie dolls that looked better," she said, swelling in anger. "With that lipstick and rouge, they made him look like a pansy!" She cursed, fiddled with the silk inside the coffin, and its touch riled her. "He didn't rate prettyin' up," she whined. "Guys like him . . ."

She paused. Maybe the looks we were giving her made her stop. I doubt that. For some reason, though, she stopped; and in the awful silence, men said, "Well, I guess I better be going." And before you could say boo, the funeral parlor was practically empty.

Mrs. Bruce lumbered to a chair, adjusted her immensity to its minute proportions, sprawled in it, and said:

"I got a right to speak my piece, ain't I?"

No one said a word.

With a sneer she had smashed our mourning to smithereens, and what was left was nothing but a hotel room for the dead. You mustn't shudder at what she did; her motives were joyless but her point, to me, was valid. We had been

200

too involved with grief to notice that this was no way to say good-by to Mr. Pickering. She saw the charade for what it was. She was right. We make, as she said, Kewpie dolls of our dead, put them on display, surround them with murmur, flood them with flowers, employ stage lighting for effect, weep, walk on tiptoes—and never get around to saying good-by.

"But funerals," the funeral director had told Mr. Duveneck and me, "are for the living. How else can we pay our respects to the dead?"

Perhaps. Mrs. Bruce had bewildered me no more than the funeral director had done. I couldn't blame her and, to be honest, I couldn't blame him. I was part of the charade, too. Mr. Duveneck and I had made it happen. The funeral director had only been our agent. Where is the right and where is the wrong? Or are they all mixed up together? Had there been a funeral director at Calvary, what would have happened there? Would that director, the agent for the then living, have murmured when the deed was done, "I can unnail Him from the cross and make Him look as good as new . . ."

". . . Now this I say, brethren, that flesh and blood cannot inherit the kingdom of God; neither doth corruption inherit incorruption. Behold, I shew you a mystery . . ."

The funeral director, as unnerved by Mrs. Bruce as were we, tried to get the show back on the road. He cleared his throat and said:

"Ah, the matter of pallbearers . . ."

"Huh?" said Mr. Duveneck.

"For the funeral tomorrow," the director spelled out.

Mr. Duveneck cracked his knuckles, looked at me, and said:

"What do you think, kid?"

"I'll be one," I said.

"Well, that makes me and you," the hostler said, and smiled at the funeral director. "That's really all we need.

It's a matter of the correct leverage. I'm a weight lifter, you know. Charles Atlas . . ."

Mr. Duveneck stopped. Mr. Richter, the third-trick foreman, was giving him awful looks.

"I think, Duveneck, that six pallbearers might be better," the foreman said. "If you'd like, I'll be one. I'd be honored to."

"Count me in," said Mr. Burkholder, the roundhouse foreman. "Now we only need two more."

He looked around the room. The only others left were Kathleen; Mrs. Bruce; the first-trick hostler, Mr. Martin; and the funeral director, who was sneaking out the door.

"Martin," said Mr. Burkholder, "I guess that makes you a pallbearer, too."

The first-trick hostler snorted an old man's snort.

"I ain't good at lifting," he complained.

"That's all right," said Mr. Duveneck. "I'll do most of it. There's an art to lifting. It's a matter of leverage. All you got to do is . . ."

"Well, Martin?" said the roundhouse foreman.

Mr. Martin bristled. "Is you *asking* or *ordering?*"

"I'm asking," said the foreman.

Mr. Martin sighed, looked trapped, and frowned.

"All right," he said. "Since you put her that way. But make sure I don't get the heavy end."

"We'll need one more," said Mr. Duveneck.

The funeral director had vanished.

From the corner of the room, Mrs. Bruce cursed. "Might as well get Beershot planted good," she said. "Count me in, boys."

"But ladies ain't supposed to . . ." Mr. Duveneck protested.

She stopped him with a string of oaths.

Then she said:

"Look around, buster. Who else is there?"

We looked around the room. She was right.

". . . *We shall not all sleep, but we shall all be changed,*

202

*in a moment, in the twinkling of an eye, at the last trump;
for the trumpet shall sound, and the dead shall be raised,
incorruptible, and we shall be changed . . ."*

Kathleen had not been scheduled to play the organ but
Mr. Pickering's funeral had become as casual and confused
as Mr. Pickering himself had been. The funeral director,
when Mr. Duveneck and I made the original arrangements,
had wanted to hire an organist, but Mr. Duveneck had asked
how much, the funeral director had changed the subject fast,
handed us a stack of 78 RPM records, and said:

"Pick out something appropriate. I've a Victrola you can
use."

On top of the stack had been "Beer Barrel Polka." When
I asked the director if he played that much at funerals, he
said he didn't play it at funerals at all. He went on to
explain that he also rented his parlor for weddings and anni-
versaries because, as he said, "to make a buck in this neighborhood, you have to work both sides of the street."

Well, Kathleen came to the funeral and when she saw
him fussing with the Victrola, she asked if she might play
the organ instead. He gave her a dirty look (he thought we
had brought in a ringer) but he said all right. I could see,
though, he wasn't pleased the way things were going. I
hoped he would be able to use Mr. Pickering's funeral as,
at least, a tax write-off.

"*. . . I am the resurrection and the life, saith the Lord;*"
the minister said at the grave. "*. . . he that believeth in me,
though he were dead, yet shall he live; and whosoever liveth
and believeth in me, shall never die . . .*"

As we stood around the grave, huddled under umbrellas,
my mind wandered. I pictured Mr. Pickering shuffling along
a street in heaven: a grimy little street lined with grimy little tenements. The smell of garbage and coffee boiling was
thick and filled the air. In one doorway dozed two sorry-
looking angels in cast-off angel clothing. Having drunk their
fill of angel wine, they were sitting in the sun, sleeping off
their eternal buzz. Other angels were children: rowdy,

grubby, and pale animals with mean faces. They were bony with hunger and filled with hate, and as Mr. Pickering passed they threw stones at him, cursed him, called him dirty names, and ordered their angel dogs to bite him.

Mr. Pickering walked into one tenement as tumbledown as the rest. Its hallways were dark and damp. Stink was everywhere. Carefully, because the banister wobbled, Mr. Pickering climbed up the stairs. On the second landing, where he paused to catch his breath, he heard—behind closed doors—two angels rage. They were man and wife. She was hopping mad. Her husband had been seen at the angel bar & grill, buying beer for an angel floozy. Mr. Pickering winced when she started throwing dishes. He hurried to the third floor.

"*. . . I know that my redeemer liveth; and that He shall stand at the latter day upon the earth: and though this body be destroyed, yet shall I see God: whom I shall see for myself, and mine eyes behold, and not as a stranger . . .*"

On the third-floor landing, Mr. Pickering hesitated. Two doors faced him: one for the flat in front and the other for the flat in the rear. The hall was too dark to read the names scrawled on either door. Downstairs they were still breaking dishes and the husband was threatening to belt his wife. "Right in your big, loud mouth!" he was shouting. Outside, drifting up from the street, were the noise of an angel dogfight, the noise of angel urchins screaming bloody murder, and far off, somewhere, the noise a freight train made. Mr. Pickering, worried, stepped up to the door of the rear flat, made an attempt to brush earth from his overalls, cleared his throat, and knocked.

"Come in, Beershot," God called. "She's open."

Mr. Pickering entered.

God, who had been sitting at the kitchen table, drinking coffee and working a crossword puzzle, got up and went to the kitchen cabinet. He got a shot glass and a bottle of Old Grand-Dad. From the refrigerator he got a cold beer,

opened it, and set these things on the table. He poured Mr.
Pickering a shot and said:

"Well, there you are: the hair of the dog that bit you."

Mr. Pickering, still standing, drank.

"Sit awhile," said God. "Make yourself at home."

God leaned over and shut off the radio. Some angels had
been singing hillbilly songs on it.

He settled back in his chair, looked at Mr. Pickering, and
said:

"Well, how did she go down there, Beershot? Did they
hurt you much?"

"She was nice down there," Mr. Pickering said.

"But they poked fun at you," God said. "I seen them doing it."

"They didn't mean to," said Mr. Pickering.

God got a sly look.

"Beershot," God said, "how was the fat women down
there?"

Mr. Pickering blushed.

"I only knowed one real well," he said. "She hated me toward the last." Feeling sorry for that, Mr. Pickering poured
himself another shot, drank it, and said:

"Is there fat ones here?"

God winked.

"They has all been waiting for you, Beershot."

Mr. Pickering looked pleased.

"For *me*, though?" he said, troubled by second thoughts.

God nodded.

"That's a nice surprise," said Mr. Pickering, relaxing.
"That's real nice."

He poured himself another drink.

God said:

"Most of you is surprised at first, and that's a fact."

Mr. Pickering, beginning to feel mellow, poured himself
another drink.

"Here is there," he said, "and there is here, ain't she, and
she always was?"

God nodded.

"She always was, Beershot," God said. "Each man rolls his own." His voice was gentle.

"For a minute," said Mr. Pickering, "I was afraid she wasn't."

"Don't be afraid no more," God said. "We has got smart-alecky angels, loudmouth angels, and them that is hard-nosed and them that is two-faced. We got guys that will make fun of you and we got a hostler as bad as Duveneck, though that Duveneck he's a jewel. We got them all. You'll be right at home here."

Mr. Pickering was silent as he digested this information.

"Well," said God, "what do you think?"

"I think," said Mr. Pickering, "I'm going to like her here."

"*. . . We brought nothing into this world, and it is certain we can carry nothing out. The Lord gave, and the Lord hath taken away; blessed be the name of the Lord.*"

The minister crumbled dirt into the hole where a stranger was. Mr. Pickering wasn't in that box. Mr. Pickering was wandering around heaven, chasing fat women who wanted to get caught, drinking Old Grand-Dad, having himself a real good time because, as they say, he was going to dwell-eth there forever.

"Well," whined Mrs. Bruce when the burying was done, "which one of you gents is going to see a lady home?"

Only she didn't exactly say it that way.

AUTHOR'S NOTE

May I thank Douglass Campbell, the railroad's public relations director in New York, and his Midwestern counterpart Farwell C. Rhodes, Jr., for allowing me to revisit the New York Central System? The men of the Indiana division (now the Illinois division) who helped me were Division Superintendent G. E. Maas, Mechanical Superintendent F. H. McHenry, District General Manager R. B. Hasselman, Riverside roundhouse General Foreman F. C. Ruskup, Riverside roundhouse Crew Dispatcher Frank Reilly (who, in the hospital and very ill, made sure via letters I saw the right men), and those two road foremen who met me at all hours and in the most obscure locations: J. Baumgardner and J. Austin. There was also the valley local crew: E. E. Schaefer was the conductor and the engineer was Bob White, who, when I was a laborer on the third trick at Riverside roundhouse, was also a laborer there. That freight train ride down Guilford Hill—from Greensburg, Indiana, to Lawrenceburg Junction—was a trip through history, thanks to its engineer, H. J. Gagen, and its fireman, E. L. Knight. Both knew more about that roller-coaster trip than did folks who all their days lived on that terrible hill. Once, I got more than I bargained for: the day I rode the diesel that pulled the Central's passenger train, the "James Whitcomb Riley." Its fireman was C. H. Larkin and its engineer was W. C. Wahlbrink, who had known my father. At Greensburg, when I got off, Mr. Wahlbrink shouted out the cab to Joe Austin and Farwell Rhodes, who were meeting me, "Take good care of him. That's R.V.'s boy . . ." For the first time in much too long I was aware of my father's death. Except for that death, my father and not Mr. Wahlbrink might have been running the "Riley."

Nonetheless, all the characters in this book—except Izzy Kadetz—are fiction. Mr. Pickering, Mr. Duveneck, George, Kathleen, and the others did not and do not exist, nor did nor do any part of them: character trait, physical appearance, or grubby attitude. Mrs. Bruce did not and does not exist—and *that* should cheer you. To those kind readers who say, "But I know who you *meant* . . ." I can only answer, "You have more imagination than I do." Also, none of the happenings happened. If they had, the New York Central System would not be in business today—and it is, very much so. But the settings—the Riverside roundhouse, Sedamsville, Sayler Park, and all the other locations—are as real as I could make them.

DICK PERRY

Oxford, Ohio
1965